California State Parks and Beaches

Travel to all the State Parks and Beaches in California.

This book belongs to _____

Call this number if found _____

My Nature Book Adventures

https://www.parks.ca.gov/parkindex

https://mynaturebookadventures.com/

Inside Your Book

The CALIFORNIA State Parks Adventure Book is part planner, part journal, and 100% your adventure! Created to include dedicated space for you to plan your journey and share your experience. Check out each of the CALIFORNIA State Parks and cross them off your MUST DO exploration list. Then look back at the experiences with your family and friends.

Plan your adventures, then share all of the fun! Decorate your pages, YOUR way. Use photos, stickers, washi tape, markers, postcards, stamps and more.

We have organized each park in alphabetical order, making it a breeze to locate the park or beach you are looking for. In this book you will find California State Parks and State Beaches.

Enjoy all of the natural beauty, unique geological features, and unusual ecosystems the CALIFORNIA State Parks offer us.

California Coast

Inside your book you will find...

ON THE LEFT SIDE OF EACH 2 PAGE SPREAD, YOU HAVE

A place to plan the details of your trip.

A section for reservation information, including refund policy, reserved dates, address, check-in and check-out times, website, phone, wifi information, and even a place for your confirmation number.

Plus an area to show how far you are traveling.

A fun color-in of the transportation modes you used during your adventures in the park.

A space to attach your favorite postcard, picture, drawing, or ticket stub.

THE RIGHT SIDE INCLUDES PARK INFORMATION AND GIVES YOU A PLACE TO SHARE THE SPECIAL MOMENTS ABOUT YOUR JOURNEY

Park Information

The county the park is located in

The year the park was established

The number of acres in the park

Some extra notes

Special Moments

Include why you went

Who went with you

When you went

An unforgettable moment

A laughable moment

A surprising moment

A shareable moment

A beautiful moment

A fun color-in of the weather you experienced during your adventures

Make it all about YOU and your journey!

Also inside is an adventure checklist to make your adventures even more memorable.

We want you to spend every moment of your trip enjoying every bit of the NEW JERSEY State Parks!

California State Map

CALIFORNIA STATE MAP

Map Legend

—— Divided Highway	Rest Area		
★ All-American Road	Welcome Center		
① California Highway	N F National Forest		
⑤ Interstate Highway	NP National Park		
⑩⑴ US Highway	NRA National Recreation Area		
✪ State Capital	SP State Park		

my nature book adventures

Mark the places on the map where you have visited. Be creative use a sticker, or just put a dot to mark your journey.

TABLE OF CONTENTS

What you will find at the parks

Ano Nuevo State Park

Website: https://www.parks.ca.gov/

TABLE OF CONTENTS

What you will find at the parks

Castle Crags State Park

Website: https://www.parks.ca.gov/

Explore more

TABLE OF CONTENTS

What you will find at the parks

Point Lobos State Park

Website: https://www.parks.ca.gov/

it's a big
world
OUT THERE
-GO-
explore

TABLE OF CONTENTS

California County Map

Mark the places on the map where you have visited. Be creative use a sticker, or just put a dot to mark your journey.

my nature book adventures

DISCOVER

TABLE OF CONTENTS

WANDERLUST

Lassen Volcano California State Parks

Website: https://www.parks.ca.gov/

COLLECT
moments
-NOT-
things

ADVENTURE CHECK LIST

- [ ] Go on a nature scavenger hunt
- [ ] Perfect your bird calls
- [ ] Have a breakfast picnic
- [ ] Go horseback riding
- [ ] Snap a selfie at a park entrance sign
- [ ] Help Someone become a Jr Ranger
- [ ] Go RVing
- [ ] Take a ranger-led tour
- [ ] Splash in a waterfall
- [ ] Stop at scenic overlooks
- [ ] Hunt for fossils
- [ ] Look for EarthCache sites
- [ ] Canoe along a river
- [ ] Go on a photography walk
- [ ] Take a nature hike
- [ ] Hunt for animal tracks
- [ ] Go kayaking
- [ ] Try rock climbing
- [ ] Visit a nature center
- [ ] Watch the sunset
- [ ] Ride a bike
- [ ] Try a night sky program
- [ ] Go geocaching
- [ ] Pitch a tent
- [ ] Photograph wildflowers

- [ ] Cast a fishing line
- [ ] Take a boat cruise across a lake
- [ ] Enjoy a scenic drive
- [ ] Snap lots of photos
- [ ] Smell the fresh air
- [ ] Arrive early for wildlife watching
- [ ] Scramble over rocks
- [ ] Eat a picnic at a scenic spot
- [ ] Go on a night hike
- [ ] Ride a historic train
- [ ] Hike to the top of a mountain
- [ ] Try a cell phone audio tour
- [ ] Enjoy a tidepool walk
- [ ] Go on a full moon ranger hike
- [ ] Go on a cave tour
- [ ] Go stargazing
- [ ] Adhere to Leave No Trace principles
- [ ] Play in the water

EXPLORE MORE

PLAN YOUR TRIP:

☐ Day Trip   ☐ Overnight Stay

Reservations required: ☐ y ☐ n

Date reservations made: _____

Refund Policy: ☐ y ☐ n Site #: _____

Confirmation #: _____

Miles to travel: _____

Time traveling: _____

RV's?: ☐ y ☐ n Largest size RV? _____

Activities Accomplished:

☐ Archery
☐ Biking
☐ Birding
☐ Boating
☐ Camping
☐ Caving
☐ Geocaching

☐ Fishing
☐ Hiking
☐ Horseback Riding
☐ Hunting
☐ Off-Roading
☐ Paddle Boarding
☐ Photography

☐ Picknicking
☐ Rock Climbing
☐ Shooting Range
☐ Snowshoeing
☐ Stargazing
☐ Swimming
☐ Tennis

☐ Walking
☐ Wildlife Watching
☐ _____
☐ _____
☐ _____
☐ _____
☐ _____

Traveling by:

☐ ☐ ☐ ☐ ☐ ☐ ☐ ☐ ☐ ☐ ☐ ☐

RESERVATION INFORMATION:

Address: _____
_____

Reserved dates: _____

Check-in time: _____ Early check-in?: ☐ y ☐ n

Check-out time: _____ Late check-out?: ☐ y ☐ n

Website: _____

Phone: _____

WiFi: _____ WiFi password: _____

Dog friendly?: ☐ y ☐ n   Open all year?: ☐ y ☐ n

Add your favorite ticket stub, postcard, photo, stamp or drawing here

LET NEW ADVENTURES
≫ BEGIN →

Ahjumawi Lava Springs State Park

County: Shasta

Established: 1975   *Acres: 5,930*

Preserves a wilderness of freshwater springs and geologically recent lava flows.

Star Rating
☆ ☆ ☆ ☆ ☆

My favorite thing about this place is... _____

Why I went ... _____

Who I went with ... _____

When I went ... _____

What I did... _____

What I saw... _____

What I learned... _____

An unforgettable moment... _____

A laughable moment... _____

A surprising moment... _____

An unforeseeable moment... _____

Wildlife spotted... _____

List
- ☐ _____
- ☐ _____
- ☐ _____
- ☐ _____
- ☐ _____
- ☐ _____
- ☐ _____
- ☐ _____
- ☐ _____
- ☐ _____
- ☐ _____
- ☐ _____
- ☐ _____
- ☐ _____
- ☐ _____
- ☐ _____
- ☐ _____
- ☐ _____
- ☐ _____
- ☐ _____

Snapped a selfie | Location... _____

Took a park sign photo? - ☐ y ☐ n

The weather was ... ☐ ☐ ☐ ☐ ☐ ☐ ☐

PLAN YOUR TRIP:

☐ Day Trip   ☐ Overnight Stay

Reservations required: ☐ y ☐ n

Date reservations made: _____

Refund Policy: ☐ y ☐ n Site #: _____

Confirmation #: _____

Miles to travel: _____

Time traveling: _____

RV's?: ☐ y ☐ n Largest size RV? _____

Activities Accomplished:

☐ Archery
☐ Biking
☐ Birding
☐ Boating
☐ Camping
☐ Caving
☐ Geocaching

☐ Fishing
☐ Hiking
☐ Horseback Riding
☐ Hunting
☐ Off-Roading
☐ Paddle Boarding
☐ Photography

☐ Picknicking
☐ Rock Climbing
☐ Shooting Range
☐ Snowshoeing
☐ Stargazing
☐ Swimming
☐ Tennis

☐ Walking
☐ Wildlife Watching
☐ _____
☐ _____
☐ _____
☐ _____
☐ _____

Traveling by:

☐ ☐ ☐ ☐ ☐ ☐ ☐ ☐ ☐ ☐ ☐ ☐

RESERVATION INFORMATION:

Address: _____
_____

Reserved dates: _____

Check-in time: _____   Early check-in?: ☐ y ☐ n

Check-out time: _____   Late check-out?: ☐ y ☐ n

Website: _____

Phone: _____

WiFi: _____ WiFi password: _____

Dog friendly?: ☐ y ☐ n   Open all year?: ☐ y ☐ n

Add your favorite ticket stub, postcard, photo, stamp or drawing here

LET NEW ADVENTURES
»» BEGIN →

Andrew Molera State Park

County: Monterey

Established: 1968

Acres: 4,766

Offers a primitive walk-in campground on the Big Sur coast.

Star Rating

☆ ☆ ☆ ☆ ☆

My favorite thing about this place is... _____

Why I went ... _____

Who I went with ... _____

When I went ... _____

What I did... _____

What I saw... _____

What I learned... _____

An unforgettable moment... _____

A laughable moment... _____

A surprising moment... _____

An unforeseeable moment... _____

Wildlife spotted... _____

List

- [ ] _____
- [ ] _____
- [ ] _____
- [ ] _____
- [ ] _____
- [ ] _____
- [ ] _____
- [ ] _____
- [ ] _____
- [ ] _____
- [ ] _____
- [ ] _____
- [ ] _____
- [ ] _____
- [ ] _____
- [ ] _____
- [ ] _____
- [ ] _____
- [ ] _____
- [ ] _____
- [ ] _____
- [ ] _____

📷 Snapped a selfie | Location...

📷 Took a park sign photo? - ☐ y ☐ n

The weather was ... ☐ ☐ ☐ ☐ ☐ ☐ ☐

PLAN YOUR TRIP:

☐ Day Trip   ☐ Overnight Stay

Reservations required: ☐ y ☐ n

Date reservations made: _____

Refund Policy: ☐ y ☐ n Site #: _____

Confirmation #: _____

Miles to travel: _____

Time traveling: _____

RV's?: ☐ y ☐ n Largest size RV? _____

Activities Accomplished:

☐ Archery	☐ Fishing	☐ Picknicking	☐ Walking
☐ Biking	☐ Hiking	☐ Rock Climbing	☐ Wildlife Watching
☐ Birding	☐ Horseback Riding	☐ Shooting Range	☐ _____
☐ Boating	☐ Hunting	☐ Snowshoeing	☐ _____
☐ Camping	☐ Off-Roading	☐ Stargazing	☐ _____
☐ Caving	☐ Paddle Boarding	☐ Swimming	☐ _____
☐ Geocaching	☐ Photography	☐ Tennis	☐ _____

Traveling by:

☐ ☐ ☐ ☐ ☐ ☐ ☐ ☐ ☐ ☐ ☐ ☐

RESERVATION INFORMATION:

Address: _____
_____

Reserved dates: _____

Check-in time: _____   Early check-in?: ☐ y ☐ n

Check-out time: _____   Late check-out?: ☐ y ☐ n

Website: _____

Phone: _____

WiFi: _____   WiFi password: _____

Dog friendly?: ☐ y ☐ n   Open all year?: ☐ y ☐ n

Add your favorite ticket stub, postcard, photo, stamp or drawing here

LET NEW ADVENTURES
≫ BEGIN →

ANGEL ISLAND STATE PARK

County: Marin and San Francisco

Established: 1955   *Acres: 756*

Interprets an island in San Francisco Bay whose history encompasses Coast Miwokprehistory, ranching, the 1910-1940 Angel Island Immigration Station, and long military use.

Star Rating
☆ ☆ ☆ ☆ ☆

My favorite thing about this place is... _____

Why I went ... _____

Who I went with ... _____

When I went ... _____

What I did... _____

What I saw... _____

What I learned... _____

An unforgettable moment... _____

A laughable moment... _____

A surprising moment... _____

An unforeseeable moment... _____

Wildlife spotted... _____

List
- ☐ _____
- ☐ _____
- ☐ _____
- ☐ _____
- ☐ _____
- ☐ _____
- ☐ _____
- ☐ _____
- ☐ _____
- ☐ _____
- ☐ _____
- ☐ _____
- ☐ _____
- ☐ _____
- ☐ _____
- ☐ _____
- ☐ _____
- ☐ _____
- ☐ _____
- ☐ _____
- ☐ _____

Snapped a selfie | Location...

Took a park sign photo? - ☐ y ☐ n

The weather was ... ☐ ☐ ☐ ☐ ☐ ☐ ☐

PLAN YOUR TRIP:

☐ Day Trip   ☐ Overnight Stay

Reservations required: ☐ y ☐ n

Date reservations made: _____

Refund Policy: ☐ y ☐ n Site #: _____

Confirmation #: _____

Miles to travel: _____

Time traveling: _____

RV's?: ☐ y ☐ n Largest size RV? _____

Activities Accomplished:

☐ Archery
☐ Biking
☐ Birding
☐ Boating
☐ Camping
☐ Caving
☐ Geocaching

☐ Fishing
☐ Hiking
☐ Horseback Riding
☐ Hunting
☐ Off-Roading
☐ Paddle Boarding
☐ Photography

☐ Picknicking
☐ Rock Climbing
☐ Shooting Range
☐ Snowshoeing
☐ Stargazing
☐ Swimming
☐ Tennis

☐ Walking
☐ Wildlife Watching
☐ _____
☐ _____
☐ _____
☐ _____
☐ _____

Traveling by:

☐ ☐ ☐ ☐ ☐ ☐ ☐ ☐ ☐ ☐ ☐ ☐

RESERVATION INFORMATION:

Address: _____
_____

Reserved dates: _____

Check-in time: _____   Early check-in?: ☐ y ☐ n

Check-out time: _____   Late check-out?: ☐ y ☐ n

Website: _____

Phone: _____

WiFi: _____   WiFi password: _____

Dog friendly?: ☐ y ☐ n   Open all year?: ☐ y ☐ n

Add your favorite ticket stub, postcard, photo, stamp or drawing here

LET NEW ADVENTURES
≫ BEGIN →

AÑO NUEVO STATE PARK

County: San Mateo

Established: 1985

Acres: 4,209

Encompasses Año Nuevo Island and Año Nuevo Point, which boasts the world's largest mainland rookery of northern elephant seals.

Star Rating
☆ ☆ ☆ ☆ ☆

My favorite thing about this place is... _____

Why I went ... _____

Who I went with ... _____

When I went ... _____

What I did... _____

What I saw... _____

What I learned... _____

An unforgettable moment... _____

A laughable moment... _____

A surprising moment... _____

An unforeseeable moment... _____

Wildlife spotted... _____

Snapped a selfie | Location... _____

Took a park sign photo? - ☐ y ☐ n

List

☐ _____
☐ _____
☐ _____
☐ _____
☐ _____
☐ _____
☐ _____
☐ _____
☐ _____
☐ _____
☐ _____
☐ _____
☐ _____
☐ _____
☐ _____
☐ _____
☐ _____
☐ _____
☐ _____
☐ _____
☐ _____
☐ _____

The weather was ...
☐ ☐ ☐ ☐ ☐ ☐ ☐

PLAN YOUR TRIP:

☐ Day Trip   ☐ Overnight Stay

Reservations required: ☐ y ☐ n

Date reservations made: _____

Refund Policy: ☐ y ☐ n Site #: _____

Confirmation #: _____

Miles to travel: _____

Time traveling: _____

RV's?: ☐ y ☐ n Largest size RV? _____

Activities Accomplished:

☐ Archery
☐ Biking
☐ Birding
☐ Boating
☐ Camping
☐ Caving
☐ Geocaching

☐ Fishing
☐ Hiking
☐ Horseback Riding
☐ Hunting
☐ Off-Roading
☐ Paddle Boarding
☐ Photography

☐ Picknicking
☐ Rock Climbing
☐ Shooting Range
☐ Snowshoeing
☐ Stargazing
☐ Swimming
☐ Tennis

☐ Walking
☐ Wildlife Watching
☐ _____
☐ _____
☐ _____
☐ _____
☐ _____

Traveling by:

☐ ☐ ☐ ☐ ☐ ☐ ☐ ☐ ☐ ☐ ☐ ☐

RESERVATION INFORMATION:

Address: _____
_____

Reserved dates: _____

Check-in time: _____ Early check-in?: ☐ y ☐ n

Check-out time: _____ Late check-out?: ☐ y ☐ n

Website: _____

Phone: _____

WiFi: _____ WiFi password: _____

Dog friendly?: ☐ y ☐ n   Open all year?: ☐ y ☐ n

Add your favorite ticket stub, postcard, photo, stamp or drawing here

LET NEW ADVENTURES
»» BEGIN →

ANZA-BORREGO DESERT STATE PARK

County: San Diego, Imperial, and Riverside

Established: 1933

Acres: 585,930

Preserves a vast tract of the Colorado Desert in California's largest state park.

Star Rating
☆ ☆ ☆ ☆ ☆

My favorite thing about this place is... _____

Why I went ... _____

Who I went with ... _____

When I went ... _____

What I did... _____

What I saw... _____

What I learned... _____

An unforgettable moment... _____

A laughable moment... _____

A surprising moment... _____

An unforeseeable moment... _____

Wildlife spotted... _____

List
- ☐ _____
- ☐ _____
- ☐ _____
- ☐ _____
- ☐ _____
- ☐ _____
- ☐ _____
- ☐ _____
- ☐ _____
- ☐ _____
- ☐ _____
- ☐ _____
- ☐ _____
- ☐ _____
- ☐ _____
- ☐ _____
- ☐ _____
- ☐ _____

Snapped a selfie | Location... _____

Took a park sign photo? - ☐ y ☐ n

The weather was ...
☐ ☐ ☐ ☐ ☐ ☐ ☐

PLAN YOUR TRIP:

☐ Day Trip   ☐ Overnight Stay

Reservations required: ☐ y ☐ n

Date reservations made: _____

Refund Policy: ☐ y ☐ n   Site #: _____

Confirmation #: _____

Miles to travel: _____

Time traveling: _____

RV's?: ☐ y ☐ n Largest size RV? _____

Activities Accomplished:

☐ Archery
☐ Biking
☐ Birding
☐ Boating
☐ Camping
☐ Caving
☐ Geocaching

☐ Fishing
☐ Hiking
☐ Horseback Riding
☐ Hunting
☐ Off-Roading
☐ Paddle Boarding
☐ Photography

☐ Picknicking
☐ Rock Climbing
☐ Shooting Range
☐ Snowshoeing
☐ Stargazing
☐ Swimming
☐ Tennis

☐ Walking
☐ Wildlife Watching
☐ _____
☐ _____
☐ _____
☐ _____
☐ _____

Traveling by:

☐ ☐ ☐ ☐ ☐ ☐ ☐ ☐ ☐ ☐ ☐ ☐

RESERVATION INFORMATION:

Address: _____
_____

Reserved dates: _____

Check-in time: _____ Early check-in?: ☐ y ☐ n

Check-out time: _____ Late check-out?: ☐ y ☐ n

Website: _____

Phone: _____

WiFi: _____ WiFi password: _____

Dog friendly?: ☐ y ☐ n   Open all year?: ☐ y ☐ n

Add your favorite ticket stub, postcard, photo, stamp or drawing here

LET NEW ADVENTURES
»» BEGIN →

Arthur B. Ripley Desert Woodland State Park

County: Los Angeles

Established: 1993   *Acres: 566*

Preserves a remnant stand of Joshua trees and junipers in the Antelope Valley.

_____
Star Rating
☆ ☆ ☆ ☆ ☆

My favorite thing about this place is... _____

Why I went ... _____

Who I went with ... _____

When I went ... _____

What I did... _____

What I saw... _____

What I learned... _____

An unforgettable moment... _____

A laughable moment... _____

A surprising moment... _____

An unforeseeable moment... _____

Wildlife spotted... _____

List
- [ ] _____
- [ ] _____
- [ ] _____
- [ ] _____
- [ ] _____
- [ ] _____
- [ ] _____
- [ ] _____
- [ ] _____
- [ ] _____
- [ ] _____
- [ ] _____
- [ ] _____
- [ ] _____
- [ ] _____
- [ ] _____
- [ ] _____
- [ ] _____

[◎] Snapped a selfie | Location...

[◎] Took a park sign photo? - ☐ y ☐ n

The weather was ... ☐ ☐ ☐ ☐ ☐ ☐ ☐

PLAN YOUR TRIP:

☐ Day Trip   ☐ Overnight Stay

Reservations required: ☐ y ☐ n

Date reservations made: _____

Refund Policy: ☐ y ☐ n Site #: _____

Confirmation #: _____

Miles to travel: _____

Time traveling: _____

RV's?: ☐ y ☐ n Largest size RV? _____

Activities Accomplished:

☐ Archery
☐ Biking
☐ Birding
☐ Boating
☐ Camping
☐ Caving
☐ Geocaching

☐ Fishing
☐ Hiking
☐ Horseback Riding
☐ Hunting
☐ Off-Roading
☐ Paddle Boarding
☐ Photography

☐ Picknicking
☐ Rock Climbing
☐ Shooting Range
☐ Snowshoeing
☐ Stargazing
☐ Swimming
☐ Tennis

☐ Walking
☐ Wildlife Watching
☐ _____
☐ _____
☐ _____
☐ _____
☐ _____

RESERVATION INFORMATION:

Address: _____
_____

Reserved dates: _____

Check-in time: _____ Early check-in?: ☐ y ☐ n

Check-out time: _____ Late check-out?: ☐ y ☐ n

Website: _____

Phone: _____

WiFi: _____ WiFi password: _____

Dog friendly?: ☐ y ☐ n   Open all year?: ☐ y ☐ n

Traveling by:

☐ ☐ ☐ ☐ ☐ ☐ ☐ ☐ ☐ ☐ ☐ ☐

Add your favorite ticket stub, postcard, photo, stamp or drawing here

LET NEW ADVENTURES
≫ BEGIN →

Bidwell-Sacramento River State Park

County: Butte and Glenn

Established: 1979   *Acres: 349*

Preserves riparian habitat on the Sacramento River and its tributary Big Chico Creek.

Star Rating

☆ ☆ ☆ ☆ ☆

My favorite thing about this place is... _____

Why I went ... _____

Who I went with ... _____

When I went ... _____

What I did... _____

What I saw... _____

What I learned... _____

An unforgettable moment... _____

A laughable moment... _____

A surprising moment... _____

An unforeseeable moment... _____

Wildlife spotted... _____

List
☐ _____
☐ _____
☐ _____
☐ _____
☐ _____
☐ _____
☐ _____
☐ _____
☐ _____
☐ _____
☐ _____
☐ _____
☐ _____
☐ _____
☐ _____
☐ _____
☐ _____
☐ _____
☐ _____
☐ _____

Snapped a selfie | Location... _____

Took a park sign photo? - ☐ y ☐ n

The weather was ...   ☐ ☐ ☐ ☐ ☐ ☐ ☐

PLAN YOUR TRIP:

RESERVATION INFORMATION:

☐ Day Trip   ☐ Overnight Stay

Reservations required: ☐ y ☐ n

Date reservations made: _____

Refund Policy: ☐ y ☐ n Site #: _____

Confirmation #: _____

Miles to travel: _____

Time traveling: _____

RV's?: ☐ y ☐ n Largest size RV? _____

Address: _____
_____

Reserved dates: _____

Check-in time: _____ Early check-in?: ☐ y ☐ n

Check-out time: _____ Late check-out?: ☐ y ☐ n

Website: _____

Phone: _____

WiFi: _____ WiFi password: _____

Dog friendly?: ☐ y ☐ n   Open all year?: ☐ y ☐ n

Activities Accomplished:

☐ Archery
☐ Biking
☐ Birding
☐ Boating
☐ Camping
☐ Caving
☐ Geocaching

☐ Fishing
☐ Hiking
☐ Horseback Riding
☐ Hunting
☐ Off-Roading
☐ Paddle Boarding
☐ Photography

☐ Picknicking
☐ Rock Climbing
☐ Shooting Range
☐ Snowshoeing
☐ Stargazing
☐ Swimming
☐ Tennis

☐ Walking
☐ Wildlife Watching
☐ _____
☐ _____
☐ _____
☐ _____
☐ _____

Traveling by:

☐ ☐ ☐ ☐ ☐ ☐ ☐ ☐ ☐ ☐ ☐ ☐

Add your favorite ticket stub, postcard, photo, stamp or drawing here

LET NEW ADVENTURES
»» BEGIN →

Big Basin Redwoods State Park

County: Santa Cruz

Established: 1902   Acres: 18,050

Established as California's first state park, to preserve coast redwoods on Waddell Creek.

Star Rating
☆ ☆ ☆ ☆ ☆

My favorite thing about this place is... _____

Why I went ... _____

Who I went with ... _____

When I went ... _____

What I did... _____

What I saw... _____

What I learned... _____

An unforgettable moment... _____

A laughable moment... _____

A surprising moment... _____

An unforeseeable moment... _____

Wildlife spotted... _____

Snapped a selfie | Location... _____

Took a park sign photo? - ☐ y ☐ n

List

- ☐ _____
- ☐ _____
- ☐ _____
- ☐ _____
- ☐ _____
- ☐ _____
- ☐ _____
- ☐ _____
- ☐ _____
- ☐ _____
- ☐ _____
- ☐ _____
- ☐ _____
- ☐ _____
- ☐ _____
- ☐ _____
- ☐ _____
- ☐ _____
- ☐ _____

The weather was ...
☐ ☐ ☐ ☐ ☐ ☐ ☐

PLAN YOUR TRIP:

RESERVATION INFORMATION:

☐ Day Trip   ☐ Overnight Stay

Reservations required: ☐ y ☐ n

Date reservations made: _____

Refund Policy: ☐ y ☐ n Site #: _____

Confirmation #: _____

Miles to travel: _____

Time traveling: _____

RV's?: ☐ y ☐ n Largest size RV? _____

Address: _____
_____

Reserved dates: _____

Check-in time: _____ Early check-in?: ☐ y ☐ n

Check-out time: _____ Late check-out?: ☐ y ☐ n

Website: _____

Phone: _____

WiFi: _____ WiFi password: _____

Dog friendly?: ☐ y ☐ n   Open all year?: ☐ y ☐ n

Activities Accomplished:

☐ Archery
☐ Biking
☐ Birding
☐ Boating
☐ Camping
☐ Caving
☐ Geocaching

☐ Fishing
☐ Hiking
☐ Horseback Riding
☐ Hunting
☐ Off-Roading
☐ Paddle Boarding
☐ Photography

☐ Picknicking
☐ Rock Climbing
☐ Shooting Range
☐ Snowshoeing
☐ Stargazing
☐ Swimming
☐ Tennis

☐ Walking
☐ Wildlife Watching
☐ _____
☐ _____
☐ _____
☐ _____
☐ _____

Traveling by:

☐ ☐ ☐ ☐ ☐ ☐ ☐ ☐ ☐ ☐ ☐ ☐

Add your favorite ticket stub, postcard, photo, stamp or drawing here

LET NEW ADVENTURES
≫ BEGIN →

Border Field State Park

County: San Diego

Established: 1972

Acres: 1,316

Occupies the southwesternmost point of the contiguous U.S., on the Mexico - United States border. Part of the Tijuana River National Estuarine Research Reserve.

Star Rating
☆☆☆☆☆

My favorite thing about this place is... _____

Why I went ... _____

Who I went with ... _____

When I went ... _____

What I did... _____

What I saw... _____

What I learned... _____

An unforgettable moment... _____

A laughable moment... _____

A surprising moment... _____

An unforeseeable moment... _____

Wildlife spotted... _____

List
- [ ] _____
- [ ] _____
- [ ] _____
- [ ] _____
- [ ] _____
- [ ] _____
- [ ] _____
- [ ] _____
- [ ] _____
- [ ] _____
- [ ] _____
- [ ] _____
- [ ] _____
- [ ] _____
- [ ] _____
- [ ] _____
- [ ] _____
- [ ] _____
- [ ] _____
- [ ] _____

Snapped a selfie | Location... _____

Took a park sign photo? - ☐ y ☐ n

The weather was ...

PLAN YOUR TRIP:

☐ Day Trip   ☐ Overnight Stay

Reservations required: ☐ y ☐ n

Date reservations made: _____

Refund Policy: ☐ y ☐ n   Site #: _____

Confirmation #: _____

Miles to travel: _____

Time traveling: _____

RV's?: ☐ y ☐ n Largest size RV? _____

Activities Accomplished:

☐ Archery
☐ Biking
☐ Birding
☐ Boating
☐ Camping
☐ Caving
☐ Geocaching

☐ Fishing
☐ Hiking
☐ Horseback Riding
☐ Hunting
☐ Off-Roading
☐ Paddle Boarding
☐ Photography

☐ Picknicking
☐ Rock Climbing
☐ Shooting Range
☐ Snowshoeing
☐ Stargazing
☐ Swimming
☐ Tennis

☐ Walking
☐ Wildlife Watching
☐ _____
☐ _____
☐ _____
☐ _____
☐ _____

Traveling by:

☐ ☐ ☐ ☐ ☐ ☐ ☐ ☐ ☐ ☐ ☐ ☐

RESERVATION INFORMATION:

Address: _____
_____

Reserved dates: _____

Check-in time: _____   Early check-in?: ☐ y ☐ n

Check-out time: _____   Late check-out?: ☐ y ☐ n

Website: _____

Phone: _____

WiFi: _____   WiFi password: _____

Dog friendly?: ☐ y ☐ n   Open all year?: ☐ y ☐ n

Add your favorite ticket stub, postcard, photo, stamp or drawing here

LET NEW ADVENTURES
≫ BEGIN →

Bothe-Napa Valley State Park

County: Napa and Sonoma

Established: 1960   *Acres:* 1,991

Contains the farthest inland coast redwoods in a California state park.

Star Rating
☆ ☆ ☆ ☆ ☆

My favorite thing about this place is... _____

Why I went ... _____

Who I went with ... _____

When I went ... _____

What I did... _____

What I saw... _____

What I learned... _____

An unforgettable moment... _____

A laughable moment... _____

A surprising moment... _____

An unforeseeable moment... _____

Wildlife spotted... _____

List
- ☐ _____
- ☐ _____
- ☐ _____
- ☐ _____
- ☐ _____
- ☐ _____
- ☐ _____
- ☐ _____
- ☐ _____
- ☐ _____
- ☐ _____
- ☐ _____
- ☐ _____
- ☐ _____
- ☐ _____
- ☐ _____
- ☐ _____
- ☐ _____
- ☐ _____

Snapped a selfie | Location...

Took a park sign photo? - ☐ y ☐ n

The weather was ... ☐ ☐ ☐ ☐ ☐ ☐ ☐

PLAN YOUR TRIP:

☐ Day Trip   ☐ Overnight Stay

Reservations required: ☐ y ☐ n

Date reservations made: _____

Refund Policy: ☐ y ☐ n Site #: _____

Confirmation #: _____

Miles to travel: _____

Time traveling: _____

RV's?: ☐ y ☐ n Largest size RV? _____

Activities Accomplished:

☐ Archery
☐ Biking
☐ Birding
☐ Boating
☐ Camping
☐ Caving
☐ Geocaching

☐ Fishing
☐ Hiking
☐ Horseback Riding
☐ Hunting
☐ Off-Roading
☐ Paddle Boarding
☐ Photography

☐ Picknicking
☐ Rock Climbing
☐ Shooting Range
☐ Snowshoeing
☐ Stargazing
☐ Swimming
☐ Tennis

☐ Walking
☐ Wildlife Watching
☐ _____
☐ _____
☐ _____
☐ _____
☐ _____

RESERVATION INFORMATION:

Address: _____
_____

Reserved dates: _____

Check-in time: _____ Early check-in?: ☐ y ☐ n

Check-out time: _____ Late check-out?: ☐ y ☐ n

Website: _____

Phone: _____

WiFi: _____ WiFi password: _____

Dog friendly?: ☐ y ☐ n   Open all year?: ☐ y ☐ n

Traveling by:

☐ ☐ ☐ ☐ ☐ ☐ ☐ ☐ ☐ ☐ ☐ ☐

Add your favorite ticket stub, postcard, photo, stamp or drawing here

LET NEW ADVENTURES
≫ BEGIN →

Burton Creek State Park

County: Placer

Established: 1976

Acres: 1,890

Offers 6 miles (9.7 km) of unpaved roadway for hiking and cross-country skiing.

Star Rating
☆☆☆☆☆

My favorite thing about this place is...

Why I went ...

Who I went with ...

When I went ...

What I did...

What I saw...

What I learned...

List

- ☐
- ☐
- ☐
- ☐
- ☐
- ☐
- ☐
- ☐
- ☐
- ☐
- ☐
- ☐
- ☐
- ☐
- ☐
- ☐
- ☐
- ☐
- ☐
- ☐
- ☐
- ☐

An unforgettable moment...

A laughable moment...

A surprising moment...

An unforeseeable moment...

Wildlife spotted...

Snapped a selfie | Location...

Took a park sign photo? - ☐ y ☐ n

The weather was ...
☐ ☐ ☐ ☐ ☐ ☐ ☐

PLAN YOUR TRIP:

RESERVATION INFORMATION:

☐ Day Trip   ☐ Overnight Stay

Reservations required: ☐ y ☐ n

Date reservations made: _____

Refund Policy: ☐ y ☐ n Site #: _____

Confirmation #: _____

Miles to travel: _____

Time traveling: _____

RV's?: ☐ y ☐ n Largest size RV? _____

Address: _____
_____

Reserved dates: _____

Check-in time: _____ Early check-in?: ☐ y ☐ n

Check-out time: _____ Late check-out?: ☐ y ☐ n

Website: _____

Phone: _____

WiFi: _____ WiFi password: _____

Dog friendly?: ☐ y ☐ n   Open all year?: ☐ y ☐ n

Activities Accomplished:

☐ Archery
☐ Biking
☐ Birding
☐ Boating
☐ Camping
☐ Caving
☐ Geocaching

☐ Fishing
☐ Hiking
☐ Horseback Riding
☐ Hunting
☐ Off-Roading
☐ Paddle Boarding
☐ Photography

☐ Picknicking
☐ Rock Climbing
☐ Shooting Range
☐ Snowshoeing
☐ Stargazing
☐ Swimming
☐ Tennis

☐ Walking
☐ Wildlife Watching
☐ _____
☐ _____
☐ _____
☐ _____
☐ _____

Traveling by:

☐ ☐ ☐ ☐ ☐ ☐ ☐ ☐ ☐ ☐ ☐ ☐

Add your favorite ticket stub, postcard, photo, stamp or drawing here

LET NEW ADVENTURES
≫ BEGIN →

Butano State Park

County: San Mateo

Established: 1956   *Acres: 4,728*

Showcases a secluded redwood-filled valley.

Star Rating
☆☆☆☆☆

My favorite thing about this place is... _____

Why I went ... _____

Who I went with ... _____

When I went ... _____

What I did... _____

What I saw... _____

What I learned... _____

An unforgettable moment... _____

A laughable moment... _____

A surprising moment... _____

An unforeseeable moment... _____

Wildlife spotted... _____

List
- ☐ _____
- ☐ _____
- ☐ _____
- ☐ _____
- ☐ _____
- ☐ _____
- ☐ _____
- ☐ _____
- ☐ _____
- ☐ _____
- ☐ _____
- ☐ _____
- ☐ _____
- ☐ _____
- ☐ _____
- ☐ _____
- ☐ _____
- ☐ _____

Snapped a selfie | Location... _____

Took a park sign photo? - ☐ y ☐ n

The weather was ... ☐ ☐ ☐ ☐ ☐ ☐ ☐

PLAN YOUR TRIP:

☐ Day Trip   ☐ Overnight Stay

Reservations required: ☐ y ☐ n

Date reservations made: _____

Refund Policy: ☐ y ☐ n   Site #: _____

Confirmation #: _____

Miles to travel: _____

Time traveling: _____

RV's?: ☐ y ☐ n Largest size RV? _____

Activities Accomplished:

☐ Archery	☐ Fishing	☐ Picknicking	☐ Walking
☐ Biking	☐ Hiking	☐ Rock Climbing	☐ Wildlife Watching
☐ Birding	☐ Horseback Riding	☐ Shooting Range	☐ _____
☐ Boating	☐ Hunting	☐ Snowshoeing	☐ _____
☐ Camping	☐ Off-Roading	☐ Stargazing	☐ _____
☐ Caving	☐ Paddle Boarding	☐ Swimming	☐ _____
☐ Geocaching	☐ Photography	☐ Tennis	☐ _____

Traveling by:

☐   ☐   ☐   ☐   ☐   ☐   ☐   ☐   ☐   ☐   ☐   ☐

RESERVATION INFORMATION:

Address: _____
_____

Reserved dates: _____

Check-in time: _____   Early check-in?: ☐ y ☐ n

Check-out time: _____   Late check-out?: ☐ y ☐ n

Website: _____

Phone: _____

WiFi: _____   WiFi password: _____

Dog friendly?: ☐ y ☐ n   Open all year?: ☐ y ☐ n

Add your favorite ticket stub, postcard, photo, stamp or drawing here

LET NEW ADVENTURES
» BEGIN →

Calaveras Big Trees State Park

County: Calaveras and Tuolumne

Established: 1931

Acres: 6,498

Protects two large groves of giant sequoias.

Star Rating
☆ ☆ ☆ ☆ ☆

My favorite thing about this place is... _____

Why I went ... _____

Who I went with ... _____

When I went ... _____

What I did... _____

What I saw... _____

What I learned... _____

An unforgettable moment... _____

A laughable moment... _____

A surprising moment... _____

An unforeseeable moment... _____

Wildlife spotted... _____

List

☐ _____
☐ _____
☐ _____
☐ _____
☐ _____
☐ _____
☐ _____
☐ _____
☐ _____
☐ _____
☐ _____
☐ _____
☐ _____
☐ _____
☐ _____
☐ _____
☐ _____
☐ _____
☐ _____

Snapped a selfie | Location... _____

Took a park sign photo? - ☐ y ☐ n

The weather was ...
☐ ☐ ☐ ☐ ☐ ☐ ☐

PLAN YOUR TRIP:

☐ Day Trip   ☐ Overnight Stay

Reservations required: ☐ y ☐ n

Date reservations made: _____

Refund Policy: ☐ y ☐ n Site #: _____

Confirmation #: _____

Miles to travel: _____

Time traveling: _____

RV's?: ☐ y ☐ n Largest size RV? _____

Activities Accomplished:

☐ Archery
☐ Biking
☐ Birding
☐ Boating
☐ Camping
☐ Caving
☐ Geocaching

☐ Fishing
☐ Hiking
☐ Horseback Riding
☐ Hunting
☐ Off-Roading
☐ Paddle Boarding
☐ Photography

☐ Picknicking
☐ Rock Climbing
☐ Shooting Range
☐ Snowshoeing
☐ Stargazing
☐ Swimming
☐ Tennis

☐ Walking
☐ Wildlife Watching
☐ _____
☐ _____
☐ _____
☐ _____
☐ _____

RESERVATION INFORMATION:

Address: _____
_____

Reserved dates: _____

Check-in time: _____ Early check-in?: ☐ y ☐ n

Check-out time: _____ Late check-out?: ☐ y ☐ n

Website: _____

Phone: _____

WiFi: _____ WiFi password: _____

Dog friendly?: ☐ y ☐ n   Open all year?: ☐ y ☐ n

Traveling by:

☐ ☐ ☐ ☐ ☐ ☐ ☐ ☐ ☐ ☐ ☐ ☐

Add your favorite ticket stub, postcard, photo, stamp or drawing here

LET NEW ADVENTURES
≫ BEGIN →

California Indian Heritage Center State Park

County: Yolo

Established: 2011   *Acres: 7.91*

Undeveloped property located in West Sacramento. Plan is for this unit to eventually replace the State Indian Museum (State Historic Park).

Star Rating
☆☆☆☆☆

My favorite thing about this place is... _____

Why I went ... _____

Who I went with ... _____

When I went ... _____

What I did... _____

What I saw... _____

What I learned... _____

An unforgettable moment... _____

A laughable moment... _____

A surprising moment... _____

An unforeseeable moment... _____

Wildlife spotted... _____

List
- [ ] _____
- [ ] _____
- [ ] _____
- [ ] _____
- [ ] _____
- [ ] _____
- [ ] _____
- [ ] _____
- [ ] _____
- [ ] _____
- [ ] _____
- [ ] _____
- [ ] _____
- [ ] _____
- [ ] _____
- [ ] _____
- [ ] _____
- [ ] _____
- [ ] _____
- [ ] _____
- [ ] _____

Snapped a selfie | Location... _____

Took a park sign photo? - ☐ y ☐ n

The weather was ... ☐ ☐ ☐ ☐ ☐ ☐ ☐

PLAN YOUR TRIP:

☐ Day Trip   ☐ Overnight Stay

Reservations required: ☐ y ☐ n

Date reservations made: _____

Refund Policy: ☐ y ☐ n Site #: _____

Confirmation #: _____

Miles to travel: _____

Time traveling: _____

RV's?: ☐ y ☐ n Largest size RV? _____

Activities Accomplished:

☐ Archery   ☐ Fishing   ☐ Picknicking   ☐ Walking
☐ Biking   ☐ Hiking   ☐ Rock Climbing   ☐ Wildlife Watching
☐ Birding   ☐ Horseback Riding ☐ Shooting Range   ☐ _____
☐ Boating   ☐ Hunting   ☐ Snowshoeing   ☐ _____
☐ Camping   ☐ Off-Roading   ☐ Stargazing   ☐ _____
☐ Caving   ☐ Paddle Boarding   ☐ Swimming   ☐ _____
☐ Geocaching   ☐ Photography   ☐ Tennis   ☐ _____

Traveling by:

☐   ☐   ☐   ☐   ☐   ☐   ☐   ☐   ☐   ☐   ☐   ☐

RESERVATION INFORMATION:

Address: _____
_____

Reserved dates: _____

Check-in time: _____ Early check-in?: ☐ y ☐ n

Check-out time: _____ Late check-out?: ☐ y ☐ n

Website: _____

Phone: _____

WiFi: _____ WiFi password: _____

Dog friendly?: ☐ y ☐ n   Open all year?: ☐ y ☐ n

Add your favorite ticket stub, postcard, photo, stamp or drawing here

LET NEW ADVENTURES
»» BEGIN →

CASTLE CRAGS STATE PARK

County: Shasta

Established: 1934

Acres: 3,905

Provides access to the Castle Crags Wilderness, with its 6,000-foot-tall (1,800 m) rock crags.

Star Rating
☆ ☆ ☆ ☆ ☆

My favorite thing about this place is... _____

Why I went ... _____

Who I went with ... _____

When I went ... _____

What I did... _____

What I saw... _____

What I learned... _____

An unforgettable moment... _____

A laughable moment... _____

A surprising moment... _____

An unforeseeable moment... _____

Wildlife spotted... _____

List
- ☐ _____
- ☐ _____
- ☐ _____
- ☐ _____
- ☐ _____
- ☐ _____
- ☐ _____
- ☐ _____
- ☐ _____
- ☐ _____
- ☐ _____
- ☐ _____
- ☐ _____
- ☐ _____
- ☐ _____
- ☐ _____
- ☐ _____
- ☐ _____
- ☐ _____
- ☐ _____
- ☐ _____

Snapped a selfie | Location... _____

Took a park sign photo? - ☐ y ☐ n

The weather was ...
☐ ☐ ☐ ☐ ☐ ☐ ☐

PLAN YOUR TRIP:

RESERVATION INFORMATION:

☐ Day Trip   ☐ Overnight Stay

Reservations required: ☐ y ☐ n

Date reservations made: _____

Refund Policy: ☐ y ☐ n Site #: _____

Confirmation #: _____

Miles to travel: _____

Time traveling: _____

RV's?: ☐ y ☐ n Largest size RV? _____

Address: _____
_____

Reserved dates: _____

Check-in time: _____ Early check-in?: ☐ y ☐ n

Check-out time: _____ Late check-out?: ☐ y ☐ n

Website: _____

Phone: _____

WiFi: _____ WiFi password: _____

Dog friendly?: ☐ y ☐ n   Open all year?: ☐ y ☐ n

Activities Accomplished:

☐ Archery
☐ Biking
☐ Birding
☐ Boating
☐ Camping
☐ Caving
☐ Geocaching

☐ Fishing
☐ Hiking
☐ Horseback Riding
☐ Hunting
☐ Off-Roading
☐ Paddle Boarding
☐ Photography

☐ Picknicking
☐ Rock Climbing
☐ Shooting Range
☐ Snowshoeing
☐ Stargazing
☐ Swimming
☐ Tennis

☐ Walking
☐ Wildlife Watching
☐ _____
☐ _____
☐ _____
☐ _____
☐ _____

Traveling by:

☐ ☐ ☐ ☐ ☐ ☐ ☐ ☐ ☐ ☐ ☐ ☐

Add your favorite ticket stub, postcard, photo, stamp or drawing here

LET NEW ADVENTURES
≫ BEGIN →

CASTLE ROCK STATE PARK

County: Santa Clara, Santa Cruz, and San Mateo

Established: 1968   *Acres: 5,242*

Encompasses a wild forest with rock climbing opportunities along the crest of the Santa Cruz Mountains.

Star Rating
☆ ☆ ☆ ☆ ☆

My favorite thing about this place is... _____

Why I went ... _____

Who I went with ... _____

When I went ... _____

What I did... _____

What I saw... _____

What I learned... _____

An unforgettable moment... _____

A laughable moment... _____

A surprising moment... _____

An unforeseeable moment... _____

Wildlife spotted... _____

List
- ☐ _____
- ☐ _____
- ☐ _____
- ☐ _____
- ☐ _____
- ☐ _____
- ☐ _____
- ☐ _____
- ☐ _____
- ☐ _____
- ☐ _____
- ☐ _____
- ☐ _____
- ☐ _____
- ☐ _____
- ☐ _____
- ☐ _____
- ☐ _____
- ☐ _____
- ☐ _____
- ☐ _____

⊙ Snapped a selfie | Location... _____

⊙ Took a park sign photo? - ☐ y ☐ n

The weather was ...
☐ ☐ ☐ ☐ ☐ ☐ ☐

PLAN YOUR TRIP:

☐ Day Trip   ☐ Overnight Stay

Reservations required: ☐ y ☐ n

Date reservations made: _____

Refund Policy: ☐ y ☐ n Site #: _____

Confirmation #: _____

Miles to travel: _____

Time traveling: _____

RV's?: ☐ y ☐ n Largest size RV? _____

Activities Accomplished:

☐ Archery   ☐ Fishing   ☐ Picknicking   ☐ Walking
☐ Biking   ☐ Hiking   ☐ Rock Climbing   ☐ Wildlife Watching
☐ Birding   ☐ Horseback Riding   ☐ Shooting Range   ☐ _____
☐ Boating   ☐ Hunting   ☐ Snowshoeing   ☐ _____
☐ Camping   ☐ Off-Roading   ☐ Stargazing   ☐ _____
☐ Caving   ☐ Paddle Boarding   ☐ Swimming   ☐ _____
☐ Geocaching   ☐ Photography   ☐ Tennis   ☐ _____

Traveling by:

☐ ☐ ☐ ☐ ☐ ☐ ☐ ☐ ☐ ☐ ☐ ☐

RESERVATION INFORMATION:

Address: _____
_____

Reserved dates: _____

Check-in time: _____ Early check-in?: ☐ y ☐ n

Check-out time: _____ Late check-out?: ☐ y ☐ n

Website: _____

Phone: _____

WiFi: _____ WiFi password: _____

Dog friendly?: ☐ y ☐ n   Open all year?: ☐ y ☐ n

Add your favorite ticket stub, postcard, photo, stamp or drawing here

LET NEW ADVENTURES
≫ BEGIN →

Caswell Memorial State Park

County: San Joaquin

Established: 1952   Acres: 258

Preserves a riparian forest along the Stanislaus River.

_____
Star Rating
☆ ☆ ☆ ☆ ☆

My favorite thing about this place is... _____

Why I went ... _____

Who I went with ... _____

When I went ... _____

What I did... _____

What I saw... _____

What I learned... _____

An unforgettable moment... _____

A laughable moment... _____

A surprising moment... _____

An unforeseeable moment... _____

Wildlife spotted... _____

📷 Snapped a selfie | Location... _____

📷 Took a park sign photo? - ☐ y ☐ n

List
- ☐ _____
- ☐ _____
- ☐ _____
- ☐ _____
- ☐ _____
- ☐ _____
- ☐ _____
- ☐ _____
- ☐ _____
- ☐ _____
- ☐ _____
- ☐ _____
- ☐ _____
- ☐ _____
- ☐ _____
- ☐ _____
- ☐ _____
- ☐ _____
- ☐ _____

The weather was ...   ☐ ☐ ☐ ☐ ☐ ☐ ☐

PLAN YOUR TRIP:

RESERVATION INFORMATION:

☐ Day Trip   ☐ Overnight Stay

Reservations required: ☐ y ☐ n

Date reservations made: _____

Refund Policy: ☐ y ☐ n Site #: _____

Confirmation #: _____

Miles to travel: _____

Time traveling: _____

RV's?: ☐ y ☐ n Largest size RV? _____

Address: _____
_____

Reserved dates: _____

Check-in time: _____ Early check-in?: ☐ y ☐ n

Check-out time: _____ Late check-out?: ☐ y ☐ n

Website: _____

Phone: _____

WiFi: _____ WiFi password: _____

Dog friendly?: ☐ y ☐ n   Open all year?: ☐ y ☐ n

Activities Accomplished:

☐ Archery
☐ Biking
☐ Birding
☐ Boating
☐ Camping
☐ Caving
☐ Geocaching

☐ Fishing
☐ Hiking
☐ Horseback Riding
☐ Hunting
☐ Off-Roading
☐ Paddle Boarding
☐ Photography

☐ Picknicking
☐ Rock Climbing
☐ Shooting Range
☐ Snowshoeing
☐ Stargazing
☐ Swimming
☐ Tennis

☐ Walking
☐ Wildlife Watching
☐ _____
☐ _____
☐ _____
☐ _____
☐ _____

Traveling by:

☐ ☐ ☐ ☐ ☐ ☐ ☐ ☐ ☐ ☐ ☐ ☐

Add your favorite ticket stub, postcard, photo, stamp or drawing here

LET NEW ADVENTURES
»» BEGIN →

CHINA CAMP STATE PARK

County: Marin

Established: 1976

Acres: 1,514

Surrounds an 1880s Chinese American shrimp-fishing village and salt marshes on San Pablo Bay.

Star Rating
☆ ☆ ☆ ☆ ☆

My favorite thing about this place is... _____

Why I went ... _____

Who I went with ... _____

When I went ... _____

What I did... _____

What I saw... _____

What I learned... _____

An unforgettable moment... _____

A laughable moment... _____

A surprising moment... _____

An unforeseeable moment... _____

Wildlife spotted... _____

Snapped a selfie | Location... _____

Took a park sign photo? - ☐ y ☐ n

List

- ☐ _____
- ☐ _____
- ☐ _____
- ☐ _____
- ☐ _____
- ☐ _____
- ☐ _____
- ☐ _____
- ☐ _____
- ☐ _____
- ☐ _____
- ☐ _____
- ☐ _____
- ☐ _____
- ☐ _____
- ☐ _____
- ☐ _____
- ☐ _____
- ☐ _____
- ☐ _____

The weather was ...
☐ ☐ ☐ ☐ ☐ ☐ ☐

PLAN YOUR TRIP:

☐ Day Trip   ☐ Overnight Stay

Reservations required: ☐ y ☐ n

Date reservations made: _____

Refund Policy: ☐ y ☐ n Site #: _____

Confirmation #: _____

Miles to travel: _____

Time traveling: _____

RV's?: ☐ y ☐ n Largest size RV? _____

Activities Accomplished:

☐ Archery
☐ Biking
☐ Birding
☐ Boating
☐ Camping
☐ Caving
☐ Geocaching

☐ Fishing
☐ Hiking
☐ Horseback Riding
☐ Hunting
☐ Off-Roading
☐ Paddle Boarding
☐ Photography

☐ Picknicking
☐ Rock Climbing
☐ Shooting Range
☐ Snowshoeing
☐ Stargazing
☐ Swimming
☐ Tennis

☐ Walking
☐ Wildlife Watching
☐ _____
☐ _____
☐ _____
☐ _____
☐ _____

RESERVATION INFORMATION:

Address: _____
_____

Reserved dates: _____

Check-in time: _____ Early check-in?: ☐ y ☐ n

Check-out time: _____ Late check-out?: ☐ y ☐ n

Website: _____

Phone: _____

WiFi: _____ WiFi password: _____

Dog friendly?: ☐ y ☐ n   Open all year?: ☐ y ☐ n

Traveling by:

☐ ☐ ☐ ☐ ☐ ☐ ☐ ☐ ☐ ☐ ☐ ☐

Add your favorite ticket stub, postcard, photo, stamp or drawing here

LET NEW ADVENTURES
»» BEGIN →

CHINO HILLS STATE PARK

County: Orange, Riverside, and San Bernardino

Established: 1981   *Acres:* 14,173

Preserves a large tract of the Chino Hills.

Star Rating
☆ ☆ ☆ ☆ ☆

My favorite thing about this place is... _____

Why I went ... _____

Who I went with ... _____

When I went ... _____

What I did... _____

What I saw... _____

What I learned... _____

An unforgettable moment... _____

A laughable moment... _____

A surprising moment... _____

An unforeseeable moment... _____

Wildlife spotted... _____

List
- ☐ _____
- ☐ _____
- ☐ _____
- ☐ _____
- ☐ _____
- ☐ _____
- ☐ _____
- ☐ _____
- ☐ _____
- ☐ _____
- ☐ _____
- ☐ _____
- ☐ _____
- ☐ _____
- ☐ _____
- ☐ _____
- ☐ _____
- ☐ _____

Snapped a selfie | Location... _____

Took a park sign photo? - ☐ y ☐ n

The weather was ... ☐ ☐ ☐ ☐ ☐ ☐ ☐

PLAN YOUR TRIP:

☐ Day Trip   ☐ Overnight Stay

Reservations required: ☐y ☐n

Date reservations made: _____

Refund Policy: ☐y ☐n Site #: _____

Confirmation #: _____

Miles to travel: _____

Time traveling: _____

RV's?: ☐y ☐n Largest size RV? _____

Activities Accomplished:

☐ Archery
☐ Biking
☐ Birding
☐ Boating
☐ Camping
☐ Caving
☐ Geocaching

☐ Fishing
☐ Hiking
☐ Horseback Riding
☐ Hunting
☐ Off-Roading
☐ Paddle Boarding
☐ Photography

☐ Picknicking
☐ Rock Climbing
☐ Shooting Range
☐ Snowshoeing
☐ Stargazing
☐ Swimming
☐ Tennis

☐ Walking
☐ Wildlife Watching
☐ _____
☐ _____
☐ _____
☐ _____
☐ _____

Traveling by:

☐ ☐ ☐ ☐ ☐ ☐ ☐ ☐ ☐ ☐ ☐ ☐

RESERVATION INFORMATION:

Address: _____

_____

Reserved dates: _____

Check-in time: _____   Early check-in?: ☐y ☐n

Check-out time: _____   Late check-out?: ☐y ☐n

Website: _____

Phone: _____

WiFi: _____   WiFi password: _____

Dog friendly?: ☐y ☐n   Open all year?: ☐y ☐n

Add your favorite ticket stub, postcard, photo, stamp or drawing here

LET NEW ADVENTURES
»» BEGIN →

CLEAR LAKE STATE PARK

County: Lake

Established: 1949

Acres: 590

Provides recreation opportunities on the southwest shore of Clear Lake, the largest freshwater lake within California's borders.

Star Rating
☆ ☆ ☆ ☆ ☆

My favorite thing about this place is... _____

Why I went ... _____

Who I went with ... _____

When I went ... _____

What I did... _____

What I saw... _____

What I learned... _____

An unforgettable moment... _____

A laughable moment... _____

A surprising moment... _____

An unforeseeable moment... _____

Wildlife spotted... _____

List
- ☐ _____
- ☐ _____
- ☐ _____
- ☐ _____
- ☐ _____
- ☐ _____
- ☐ _____
- ☐ _____
- ☐ _____
- ☐ _____
- ☐ _____
- ☐ _____
- ☐ _____
- ☐ _____
- ☐ _____
- ☐ _____
- ☐ _____
- ☐ _____
- ☐ _____
- ☐ _____

Snapped a selfie | Location... _____

Took a park sign photo? - ☐ y ☐ n

The weather was ...
☐ ☐ ☐ ☐ ☐ ☐ ☐

PLAN YOUR TRIP:

☐ Day Trip   ☐ Overnight Stay

Reservations required: ☐ y ☐ n

Date reservations made: _____

Refund Policy: ☐ y ☐ n   Site #: _____

Confirmation #: _____

Miles to travel: _____

Time traveling: _____

RV's?: ☐ y ☐ n Largest size RV? _____

Activities Accomplished:

☐ Archery	☐ Fishing	☐ Picknicking	☐ Walking
☐ Biking	☐ Hiking	☐ Rock Climbing	☐ Wildlife Watching
☐ Birding	☐ Horseback Riding	☐ Shooting Range	☐ _____
☐ Boating	☐ Hunting	☐ Snowshoeing	☐ _____
☐ Camping	☐ Off-Roading	☐ Stargazing	☐ _____
☐ Caving	☐ Paddle Boarding	☐ Swimming	☐ _____
☐ Geocaching	☐ Photography	☐ Tennis	☐ _____

Traveling by:

☐ ☐ ☐ ☐ ☐ ☐ ☐ ☐ ☐ ☐ ☐ ☐

RESERVATION INFORMATION:

Address: _____
_____

Reserved dates: _____

Check-in time: _____   Early check-in?: ☐ y ☐ n

Check-out time: _____   Late check-out?: ☐ y ☐ n

Website: _____

Phone: _____

WiFi: _____   WiFi password: _____

Dog friendly?: ☐ y ☐ n   Open all year?: ☐ y ☐ n

Add your favorite ticket stub, postcard, photo, stamp or drawing here

LET NEW ADVENTURES
>>> BEGIN →

CRYSTAL COVE STATE PARK

County: Orange

Established: 1979

Acres: 3,936

Encompasses cliffbound coastline, inland chaparral canyons, and the NRHP-listed Crystal Cove Historic District of 1920s and 30s beach cottages.

Star Rating
☆ ☆ ☆ ☆ ☆

My favorite thing about this place is... _____

Why I went ... _____

Who I went with ... _____

When I went ... _____

What I did... _____

What I saw... _____

What I learned... _____

An unforgettable moment... _____

A laughable moment... _____

A surprising moment... _____

An unforeseeable moment... _____

Wildlife spotted... _____

List
- ☐ _____
- ☐ _____
- ☐ _____
- ☐ _____
- ☐ _____
- ☐ _____
- ☐ _____
- ☐ _____
- ☐ _____
- ☐ _____
- ☐ _____
- ☐ _____
- ☐ _____
- ☐ _____
- ☐ _____
- ☐ _____
- ☐ _____
- ☐ _____

Snapped a selfie | Location... _____

Took a park sign photo? - ☐ y ☐ n

The weather was ...
☐ ☐ ☐ ☐ ☐ ☐ ☐

PLAN YOUR TRIP:

RESERVATION INFORMATION:

☐ Day Trip   ☐ Overnight Stay

Reservations required: ☐ y ☐ n

Date reservations made: _____

Refund Policy: ☐ y ☐ n   Site #: _____

Confirmation #: _____

Miles to travel: _____

Time traveling: _____

RV's?: ☐ y ☐ n Largest size RV? _____

Activities Accomplished:

Address: _____

Reserved dates: _____

Check-in time: _____   Early check-in?: ☐ y ☐ n

Check-out time: _____   Late check-out?: ☐ y ☐ n

Website: _____

Phone: _____

WiFi: _____   WiFi password: _____

Dog friendly?: ☐ y ☐ n   Open all year?: ☐ y ☐ n

☐ Archery
☐ Biking
☐ Birding
☐ Boating
☐ Camping
☐ Caving
☐ Geocaching

☐ Fishing
☐ Hiking
☐ Horseback Riding
☐ Hunting
☐ Off-Roading
☐ Paddle Boarding
☐ Photography

☐ Picknicking
☐ Rock Climbing
☐ Shooting Range
☐ Snowshoeing
☐ Stargazing
☐ Swimming
☐ Tennis

☐ Walking
☐ Wildlife Watching
☐ _____
☐ _____
☐ _____
☐ _____
☐ _____

Traveling by:

☐ ☐ ☐ ☐ ☐ ☐ ☐ ☐ ☐ ☐ ☐ ☐

Add your favorite ticket stub, postcard, photo, stamp or drawing here

LET NEW ADVENTURES
≫ BEGIN →

Cuyamaca Rancho State Park

County: San Diego

Established: 1933

Acres: 24,693

Preserves an expansive tract of forests and meadows above 5,000 feet (1,500 m) in the Laguna Mountains, on the former Rancho Cuyamaca.

Star Rating
☆ ☆ ☆ ☆ ☆

My favorite thing about this place is... _____

Why I went ... _____

Who I went with ... _____

When I went ... _____

What I did... _____

What I saw... _____

What I learned... _____

An unforgettable moment... _____

A laughable moment... _____

A surprising moment... _____

An unforeseeable moment... _____

Wildlife spotted... _____

 Snapped a selfie | Location... _____

Took a park sign photo? - ☐ y ☐ n

List
- ☐ _____
- ☐ _____
- ☐ _____
- ☐ _____
- ☐ _____
- ☐ _____
- ☐ _____
- ☐ _____
- ☐ _____
- ☐ _____
- ☐ _____
- ☐ _____
- ☐ _____
- ☐ _____
- ☐ _____
- ☐ _____
- ☐ _____
- ☐ _____

The weather was ...

☐ ☐ ☐ ☐ ☐ ☐ ☐

PLAN YOUR TRIP:

☐ Day Trip   ☐ Overnight Stay

Reservations required: ☐ y ☐ n

Date reservations made: _____

Refund Policy: ☐ y ☐ n   Site #: _____

Confirmation #: _____

Miles to travel: _____

Time traveling: _____

RV's?: ☐ y ☐ n Largest size RV? _____

Activities Accomplished:

☐ Archery
☐ Biking
☐ Birding
☐ Boating
☐ Camping
☐ Caving
☐ Geocaching

☐ Fishing
☐ Hiking
☐ Horseback Riding
☐ Hunting
☐ Off-Roading
☐ Paddle Boarding
☐ Photography

☐ Picknicking
☐ Rock Climbing
☐ Shooting Range
☐ Snowshoeing
☐ Stargazing
☐ Swimming
☐ Tennis

☐ Walking
☐ Wildlife Watching
☐ _____
☐ _____
☐ _____
☐ _____
☐ _____

Traveling by:

☐ ☐ ☐ ☐ ☐ ☐ ☐ ☐ ☐ ☐ ☐ ☐

RESERVATION INFORMATION:

Address: _____
_____

Reserved dates: _____

Check-in time: _____   Early check-in?: ☐ y ☐ n

Check-out time: _____ Late check-out?: ☐ y ☐ n

Website: _____

Phone: _____

WiFi: _____   WiFi password: _____

Dog friendly?: ☐ y ☐ n   Open all year?: ☐ y ☐ n

Add your favorite ticket stub, postcard, photo, stamp or drawing here

LET NEW ADVENTURES
≫ BEGIN →

D. L. Bliss State Park

County: El Dorado

Established: 1929

Acres: 2,149

Features a balancing rock and the Rubicon Point Light on the shore of Lake Tahoe.

Star Rating
☆ ☆ ☆ ☆ ☆

My favorite thing about this place is... _____

Why I went ... _____

Who I went with ... _____

When I went ... _____

What I did... _____

What I saw... _____

What I learned... _____

An unforgettable moment... _____

A laughable moment... _____

A surprising moment... _____

An unforeseeable moment... _____

Wildlife spotted... _____

📷 Snapped a selfie | Location... _____

📷 Took a park sign photo? - ☐ y ☐ n

List

☐ _____
☐ _____
☐ _____
☐ _____
☐ _____
☐ _____
☐ _____
☐ _____
☐ _____
☐ _____
☐ _____
☐ _____
☐ _____
☐ _____
☐ _____
☐ _____
☐ _____
☐ _____

The weather was ... ☐ ☐ ☐ ☐ ☐ ☐ ☐

PLAN YOUR TRIP:

☐ Day Trip   ☐ Overnight Stay

Reservations required: ☐ y ☐ n

Date reservations made: _____

Refund Policy: ☐ y ☐ n Site #: _____

Confirmation #: _____

Miles to travel: _____

Time traveling: _____

RV's?: ☐ y ☐ n Largest size RV? _____

Activities Accomplished:

☐ Archery
☐ Biking
☐ Birding
☐ Boating
☐ Camping
☐ Caving
☐ Geocaching

☐ Fishing
☐ Hiking
☐ Horseback Riding
☐ Hunting
☐ Off-Roading
☐ Paddle Boarding
☐ Photography

☐ Picknicking
☐ Rock Climbing
☐ Shooting Range
☐ Snowshoeing
☐ Stargazing
☐ Swimming
☐ Tennis

☐ Walking
☐ Wildlife Watching
☐ _____
☐ _____
☐ _____
☐ _____
☐ _____

RESERVATION INFORMATION:

Address: _____
_____

Reserved dates: _____

Check-in time: _____ Early check-in?: ☐ y ☐ n

Check-out time: _____ Late check-out?: ☐ y ☐ n

Website: _____

Phone: _____

WiFi: _____ WiFi password: _____

Dog friendly?: ☐ y ☐ n   Open all year?: ☐ y ☐ n

Traveling by:

☐ ☐ ☐ ☐ ☐ ☐ ☐ ☐ ☐ ☐ ☐ ☐

Add your favorite ticket stub, postcard, photo, stamp or drawing here

LET NEW ADVENTURES
≫ BEGIN →

DEL NORTE COAST REDWOODS STATE PARK

County: Del Norte

Established: 1925

Acres: 31,261

Preserves old-growth coast redwoods and is managed cooperatively with RNSP.

Star Rating
☆ ☆ ☆ ☆ ☆

My favorite thing about this place is... _____

Why I went ... _____

Who I went with ... _____

When I went ... _____

What I did... _____

What I saw... _____

What I learned... _____

An unforgettable moment... _____

A laughable moment... _____

A surprising moment... _____

An unforeseeable moment... _____

Wildlife spotted... _____

Snapped a selfie | Location... _____

Took a park sign photo? - ☐ y ☐ n

List
- ☐ _____
- ☐ _____
- ☐ _____
- ☐ _____
- ☐ _____
- ☐ _____
- ☐ _____
- ☐ _____
- ☐ _____
- ☐ _____
- ☐ _____
- ☐ _____
- ☐ _____
- ☐ _____
- ☐ _____
- ☐ _____
- ☐ _____
- ☐ _____
- ☐ _____
- ☐ _____
- ☐ _____
- ☐ _____

The weather was ...
☐ ☐ ☐ ☐ ☐ ☐ ☐

PLAN YOUR TRIP:

RESERVATION INFORMATION:

☐ Day Trip   ☐ Overnight Stay

Reservations required: ☐ y ☐ n

Date reservations made: _____

Refund Policy: ☐ y ☐ n Site #: _____

Confirmation #: _____

Miles to travel: _____

Time traveling: _____

RV's?: ☐ y ☐ n Largest size RV? _____

Address: _____
_____

Reserved dates: _____

Check-in time: _____ Early check-in?: ☐ y ☐ n

Check-out time: _____ Late check-out?: ☐ y ☐ n

Website: _____

Phone: _____

WiFi: _____ WiFi password: _____

Dog friendly?: ☐ y ☐ n   Open all year?: ☐ y ☐ n

Activities Accomplished:

☐ Archery
☐ Biking
☐ Birding
☐ Boating
☐ Camping
☐ Caving
☐ Geocaching

☐ Fishing
☐ Hiking
☐ Horseback Riding
☐ Hunting
☐ Off-Roading
☐ Paddle Boarding
☐ Photography

☐ Picknicking
☐ Rock Climbing
☐ Shooting Range
☐ Snowshoeing
☐ Stargazing
☐ Swimming
☐ Tennis

☐ Walking
☐ Wildlife Watching
☐ _____
☐ _____
☐ _____
☐ _____
☐ _____

Traveling by:

☐   ☐   ☐   ☐   ☐   ☐   ☐   ☐   ☐   ☐   ☐   ☐

Add your favorite ticket stub, postcard, photo, stamp or drawing here

LET NEW ADVENTURES
≫ BEGIN →

Donner Memorial State Park

County: Nevada and Placer

Established: 1928   Acres: 3,293

Interprets the site where the Donner Party was trapped by weather in the Sierra Nevadaduring the winter of 1846-1847, now a National Historic Landmark.

Star Rating

☆ ☆ ☆ ☆ ☆

My favorite thing about this place is... _____

Why I went ... _____

Who I went with ... _____

When I went ... _____

What I did... _____

What I saw... _____

What I learned... _____

An unforgettable moment... _____

A laughable moment... _____

A surprising moment... _____

An unforeseeable moment... _____

Wildlife spotted... _____

List

☐ _____
☐ _____
☐ _____
☐ _____
☐ _____
☐ _____
☐ _____
☐ _____
☐ _____
☐ _____
☐ _____
☐ _____
☐ _____
☐ _____
☐ _____
☐ _____
☐ _____
☐ _____

Snapped a selfie | Location... _____

Took a park sign photo? - ☐ y ☐ n

The weather was ...   ☐ ☐ ☐ ☐ ☐ ☐ ☐

PLAN YOUR TRIP:

☐ Day Trip   ☐ Overnight Stay

Reservations required: ☐ y ☐ n

Date reservations made: _____

Refund Policy: ☐ y ☐ n Site #: _____

Confirmation #: _____

Miles to travel: _____

Time traveling: _____

RV's?: ☐ y ☐ n Largest size RV? _____

Activities Accomplished:

☐ Archery
☐ Biking
☐ Birding
☐ Boating
☐ Camping
☐ Caving
☐ Geocaching

☐ Fishing
☐ Hiking
☐ Horseback Riding
☐ Hunting
☐ Off-Roading
☐ Paddle Boarding
☐ Photography

☐ Picknicking
☐ Rock Climbing
☐ Shooting Range
☐ Snowshoeing
☐ Stargazing
☐ Swimming
☐ Tennis

☐ Walking
☐ Wildlife Watching
☐ _____
☐ _____
☐ _____
☐ _____
☐ _____

RESERVATION INFORMATION:

Address: _____
_____

Reserved dates: _____

Check-in time: _____ Early check-in?: ☐ y ☐ n

Check-out time: _____ Late check-out?: ☐ y ☐ n

Website: _____

Phone: _____

WiFi: _____ WiFi password: _____

Dog friendly?: ☐ y ☐ n   Open all year?: ☐ y ☐ n

Traveling by:

☐ ☐ ☐ ☐ ☐ ☐ ☐ ☐ ☐ ☐ ☐ ☐

Add your favorite ticket stub, postcard, photo, stamp or drawing here

LET NEW ADVENTURES
≫ BEGIN →

Ed Z'berg Sugar Pine Point State Park

County: El Dorado

Established: 1965   Acres: 2,324

Comprises the Lake Tahoe estate and 1903 summer home of banker Isaias W. Hellman.

Star Rating
☆ ☆ ☆ ☆ ☆

My favorite thing about this place is... _____

Why I went ... _____

Who I went with ... _____

When I went ... _____

What I did... _____

What I saw... _____

What I learned... _____

An unforgettable moment... _____

A laughable moment... _____

A surprising moment... _____

An unforeseeable moment... _____

Wildlife spotted... _____

📷 Snapped a selfie | Location... _____

📷 Took a park sign photo? - ☐ y ☐ n

List
- ☐ _____
- ☐ _____
- ☐ _____
- ☐ _____
- ☐ _____
- ☐ _____
- ☐ _____
- ☐ _____
- ☐ _____
- ☐ _____
- ☐ _____
- ☐ _____
- ☐ _____
- ☐ _____
- ☐ _____
- ☐ _____
- ☐ _____
- ☐ _____

The weather was ... ☐ ☐ ☐ ☐ ☐ ☐ ☐

PLAN YOUR TRIP:

☐ Day Trip   ☐ Overnight Stay

Reservations required: ☐ y ☐ n

Date reservations made: _____

Refund Policy: ☐ y ☐ n Site #: _____

Confirmation #: _____

Miles to travel: _____

Time traveling: _____

RV's?: ☐ y ☐ n Largest size RV? _____

Activities Accomplished:

☐ Archery
☐ Biking
☐ Birding
☐ Boating
☐ Camping
☐ Caving
☐ Geocaching

☐ Fishing
☐ Hiking
☐ Horseback Riding
☐ Hunting
☐ Off-Roading
☐ Paddle Boarding
☐ Photography

☐ Picknicking
☐ Rock Climbing
☐ Shooting Range
☐ Snowshoeing
☐ Stargazing
☐ Swimming
☐ Tennis

☐ Walking
☐ Wildlife Watching
☐ _____
☐ _____
☐ _____
☐ _____
☐ _____

Traveling by:

☐ ☐ ☐ ☐ ☐ ☐ ☐ ☐ ☐ ☐ ☐ ☐

RESERVATION INFORMATION:

Address: _____
_____

Reserved dates: _____

Check-in time: _____   Early check-in?: ☐ y ☐ n

Check-out time: _____   Late check-out?: ☐ y ☐ n

Website: _____

Phone: _____

WiFi: _____   WiFi password: _____

Dog friendly?: ☐ y ☐ n   Open all year?: ☐ y ☐ n

Add your favorite ticket stub, postcard, photo, stamp or drawing here

LET NEW ADVENTURES
»» BEGIN →

EMERALD BAY STATE PARK

County: El Dorado

Established: 1953

Acres: 1,533

Contains Lake Tahoe's Emerald Bay and Fannette Island plus the 1929 Vikingsholmmansion, which is on the NRHP.

Star Rating

☆ ☆ ☆ ☆ ☆

My favorite thing about this place is... _____

Why I went ... _____

Who I went with ... _____

When I went ... _____

What I did... _____

What I saw... _____

What I learned... _____

An unforgettable moment... _____

A laughable moment... _____

A surprising moment... _____

An unforeseeable moment... _____

Wildlife spotted... _____

○ Snapped a selfie | Location... _____

○ Took a park sign photo? - ☐ y ☐ n

List

☐ _____
☐ _____
☐ _____
☐ _____
☐ _____
☐ _____
☐ _____
☐ _____
☐ _____
☐ _____
☐ _____
☐ _____
☐ _____
☐ _____
☐ _____
☐ _____
☐ _____
☐ _____

The weather was ...

☐ ☐ ☐ ☐ ☐ ☐ ☐

PLAN YOUR TRIP:

☐ Day Trip   ☐ Overnight Stay

Reservations required: ☐ y ☐ n

Date reservations made: _____

Refund Policy: ☐ y ☐ n Site #: _____

Confirmation #: _____

Miles to travel: _____

Time traveling: _____

RV's?: ☐ y ☐ n Largest size RV? _____

Activities Accomplished:

☐ Archery
☐ Biking
☐ Birding
☐ Boating
☐ Camping
☐ Caving
☐ Geocaching

☐ Fishing
☐ Hiking
☐ Horseback Riding
☐ Hunting
☐ Off-Roading
☐ Paddle Boarding
☐ Photography

☐ Picknicking
☐ Rock Climbing
☐ Shooting Range
☐ Snowshoeing
☐ Stargazing
☐ Swimming
☐ Tennis

☐ Walking
☐ Wildlife Watching
☐ _____
☐ _____
☐ _____
☐ _____
☐ _____

Traveling by:

☐ ☐ ☐ ☐ ☐ ☐ ☐ ☐ ☐ ☐ ☐ ☐

RESERVATION INFORMATION:

Address: _____
_____

Reserved dates: _____

Check-in time: _____ Early check-in?: ☐ y ☐ n

Check-out time: _____ Late check-out?: ☐ y ☐ n

Website: _____

Phone: _____

WiFi: _____ WiFi password: _____

Dog friendly?: ☐ y ☐ n   Open all year?: ☐ y ☐ n

Add your favorite ticket stub, postcard, photo, stamp or drawing here

LET NEW ADVENTURES
>> BEGIN →

Estero Bluffs State Park

County: San Luis Obispo

Established: *2000*   *Acres: 353*

Preserves diverse coastal habitats on Estero Bay.

Star Rating
☆ ☆ ☆ ☆ ☆

My favorite thing about this place is... _____

Why I went ... _____

Who I went with ... _____

When I went ... _____

What I did... _____

What I saw... _____

What I learned... _____

An unforgettable moment... _____

A laughable moment... _____

A surprising moment... _____

An unforeseeable moment... _____

Wildlife spotted... _____

List
- [ ] _____
- [ ] _____
- [ ] _____
- [ ] _____
- [ ] _____
- [ ] _____
- [ ] _____
- [ ] _____
- [ ] _____
- [ ] _____
- [ ] _____
- [ ] _____
- [ ] _____
- [ ] _____
- [ ] _____
- [ ] _____
- [ ] _____
- [ ] _____

Snapped a selfie | Location... _____

Took a park sign photo? - ☐ y ☐ n

The weather was ...
☐ ☐ ☐ ☐ ☐ ☐ ☐

PLAN YOUR TRIP:

☐ Day Trip   ☐ Overnight Stay

Reservations required: ☐ y ☐ n

Date reservations made: _____

Refund Policy: ☐ y ☐ n Site #: _____

Confirmation #: _____

Miles to travel: _____

Time traveling: _____

RV's?: ☐ y ☐ n Largest size RV? _____

Activities Accomplished:

☐ Archery
☐ Biking
☐ Birding
☐ Boating
☐ Camping
☐ Caving
☐ Geocaching

☐ Fishing
☐ Hiking
☐ Horseback Riding
☐ Hunting
☐ Off-Roading
☐ Paddle Boarding
☐ Photography

☐ Picknicking
☐ Rock Climbing
☐ Shooting Range
☐ Snowshoeing
☐ Stargazing
☐ Swimming
☐ Tennis

☐ Walking
☐ Wildlife Watching
☐ _____
☐ _____
☐ _____
☐ _____
☐ _____

RESERVATION INFORMATION:

Address: _____
_____

Reserved dates: _____

Check-in time: _____ Early check-in?: ☐ y ☐ n

Check-out time: _____ Late check-out?: ☐ y ☐ n

Website: _____

Phone: _____

WiFi: _____   WiFi password: _____

Dog friendly?: ☐ y ☐ n   Open all year?: ☐ y ☐ n

Traveling by:

☐ ☐ ☐ ☐ ☐ ☐ ☐ ☐ ☐ ☐ ☐ ☐

Add your favorite ticket stub, postcard, photo, stamp or drawing here

LET NEW ADVENTURES
»» BEGIN →

THE FOREST OF NISENE MARKS STATE PARK

County: Santa Cruz

Established: 1963   *Acres: 10,223*

Preserves a tract of secondary forest donated by the family of former owner Nisene Marks.

Star Rating
☆ ☆ ☆ ☆ ☆

My favorite thing about this place is... _____

Why I went ... _____

Who I went with ... _____

When I went ... _____

What I did... _____

What I saw... _____

What I learned... _____

An unforgettable moment... _____

A laughable moment... _____

A surprising moment... _____

An unforeseeable moment... _____

Wildlife spotted... _____

List

☐ _____
☐ _____
☐ _____
☐ _____
☐ _____
☐ _____
☐ _____
☐ _____
☐ _____
☐ _____
☐ _____
☐ _____
☐ _____
☐ _____
☐ _____
☐ _____
☐ _____
☐ _____
☐ _____

Snapped a selfie | Location... _____

Took a park sign photo? - ☐ y ☐ n

The weather was ...   ☐ ☐ ☐ ☐ ☐ ☐ ☐

PLAN YOUR TRIP:

☐ Day Trip   ☐ Overnight Stay

Reservations required: ☐ y ☐ n

Date reservations made: _____

Refund Policy: ☐ y ☐ n Site #: _____

Confirmation #: _____

Miles to travel: _____

Time traveling: _____

RV's?: ☐ y ☐ n Largest size RV? _____

Activities Accomplished:

☐ Archery
☐ Biking
☐ Birding
☐ Boating
☐ Camping
☐ Caving
☐ Geocaching

☐ Fishing
☐ Hiking
☐ Horseback Riding
☐ Hunting
☐ Off-Roading
☐ Paddle Boarding
☐ Photography

☐ Picknicking
☐ Rock Climbing
☐ Shooting Range
☐ Snowshoeing
☐ Stargazing
☐ Swimming
☐ Tennis

☐ Walking
☐ Wildlife Watching
☐ _____
☐ _____
☐ _____
☐ _____
☐ _____

Traveling by:

☐ ☐ ☐ ☐ ☐ ☐ ☐ ☐ ☐ ☐ ☐ ☐

RESERVATION INFORMATION:

Address: _____
_____

Reserved dates: _____

Check-in time: _____ Early check-in?: ☐ y ☐ n

Check-out time: _____ Late check-out?: ☐ y ☐ n

Website: _____

Phone: _____

WiFi: _____ WiFi password: _____

Dog friendly?: ☐ y ☐ n   Open all year?: ☐ y ☐ n

Add your favorite ticket stub, postcard, photo, stamp or drawing here

LET NEW ADVENTURES
»> BEGIN →

Fort Ord Dunes State Park

County: Monterey

Established: 2009   *Acres: 980*

Reclaims coastline overlooking Monterey Bay on former property of the decommissioned Fort Ord.

Star Rating
☆☆☆☆☆

My favorite thing about this place is... _____

Why I went ... _____

Who I went with ... _____

When I went ... _____

What I did... _____

What I saw... _____

What I learned... _____

An unforgettable moment... _____

A laughable moment... _____

A surprising moment... _____

An unforeseeable moment... _____

Wildlife spotted... _____

List
- ☐ _____
- ☐ _____
- ☐ _____
- ☐ _____
- ☐ _____
- ☐ _____
- ☐ _____
- ☐ _____
- ☐ _____
- ☐ _____
- ☐ _____
- ☐ _____
- ☐ _____
- ☐ _____
- ☐ _____
- ☐ _____
- ☐ _____
- ☐ _____
- ☐ _____

Snapped a selfie | Location... _____

Took a park sign photo? - ☐ y ☐ n

The weather was ... ☐ ☐ ☐ ☐ ☐ ☐ ☐

PLAN YOUR TRIP:

RESERVATION INFORMATION:

☐ Day Trip   ☐ Overnight Stay

Reservations required: ☐ y ☐ n

Date reservations made: _____

Refund Policy: ☐ y ☐ n Site #: _____

Confirmation #: _____

Miles to travel: _____

Time traveling: _____

RV's?: ☐ y ☐ n Largest size RV? _____

Address: _____

_____

Reserved dates: _____

Check-in time: _____ Early check-in?: ☐ y ☐ n

Check-out time: _____ Late check-out?: ☐ y ☐ n

Website: _____

Phone: _____

WiFi: _____ WiFi password: _____

Dog friendly?: ☐ y ☐ n   Open all year?: ☐ y ☐ n

Activities Accomplished:

☐ Archery
☐ Biking
☐ Birding
☐ Boating
☐ Camping
☐ Caving
☐ Geocaching

☐ Fishing
☐ Hiking
☐ Horseback Riding
☐ Hunting
☐ Off-Roading
☐ Paddle Boarding
☐ Photography

☐ Picknicking
☐ Rock Climbing
☐ Shooting Range
☐ Snowshoeing
☐ Stargazing
☐ Swimming
☐ Tennis

☐ Walking
☐ Wildlife Watching
☐ _____
☐ _____
☐ _____
☐ _____
☐ _____

Traveling by:

☐ ☐ ☐ ☐ ☐ ☐ ☐ ☐ ☐ ☐ ☐ ☐

Add your favorite ticket stub, postcard, photo, stamp or drawing here

LET NEW ADVENTURES
≫ BEGIN →

FREMONT PEAK STATE PARK

County: Monterey and San Benito

Established: 1934

Acres: 162

Provides views of the surrounding landscape from atop Fremont Peak and of the night sky from the Fremont Peak Observatory.

Star Rating
☆ ☆ ☆ ☆ ☆

My favorite thing about this place is... _____

Why I went ... _____

Who I went with ... _____

When I went ... _____

What I did... _____

What I saw... _____

What I learned... _____

An unforgettable moment... _____

A laughable moment... _____

A surprising moment... _____

An unforeseeable moment... _____

Wildlife spotted... _____

📷 Snapped a selfie | Location... _____

📷 Took a park sign photo? - ☐ y ☐ n

List
- ☐ _____
- ☐ _____
- ☐ _____
- ☐ _____
- ☐ _____
- ☐ _____
- ☐ _____
- ☐ _____
- ☐ _____
- ☐ _____
- ☐ _____
- ☐ _____
- ☐ _____
- ☐ _____
- ☐ _____
- ☐ _____
- ☐ _____
- ☐ _____
- ☐ _____
- ☐ _____

The weather was ... ☐ ☐ ☐ ☐ ☐ ☐ ☐

PLAN YOUR TRIP:

☐ Day Trip   ☐ Overnight Stay

Reservations required: ☐ y ☐ n

Date reservations made: _____

Refund Policy: ☐ y ☐ n Site #: _____

Confirmation #: _____

Miles to travel: _____

Time traveling: _____

RV's?: ☐ y ☐ n Largest size RV? _____

Activities Accomplished:

☐ Archery   ☐ Fishing   ☐ Picknicking   ☐ Walking
☐ Biking   ☐ Hiking   ☐ Rock Climbing   ☐ Wildlife Watching
☐ Birding   ☐ Horseback Riding   ☐ Shooting Range   ☐ _____
☐ Boating   ☐ Hunting   ☐ Snowshoeing   ☐ _____
☐ Camping   ☐ Off-Roading   ☐ Stargazing   ☐ _____
☐ Caving   ☐ Paddle Boarding   ☐ Swimming   ☐ _____
☐ Geocaching   ☐ Photography   ☐ Tennis   ☐ _____

Traveling by:

☐   ☐   ☐   ☐   ☐   ☐   ☐   ☐   ☐   ☐   ☐   ☐

RESERVATION INFORMATION:

Address: _____
_____

Reserved dates: _____

Check-in time: _____   Early check-in?: ☐ y ☐ n

Check-out time: _____   Late check-out?: ☐ y ☐ n

Website: _____

Phone: _____

WiFi: _____   WiFi password: _____

Dog friendly?: ☐ y ☐ n   Open all year?: ☐ y ☐ n

Add your favorite ticket stub, postcard, photo, stamp or drawing here

LET NEW ADVENTURES
»› BEGIN →

Garrapata State Park

County: Monterey

Established: 1979

Acres: 2,939

Preserves a largely hidden stretch of wild coast.

Star Rating

☆ ☆ ☆ ☆ ☆

My favorite thing about this place is... _____

Why I went ... _____

Who I went with ... _____

When I went ... _____

What I did... _____

What I saw... _____

What I learned... _____

An unforgettable moment... _____

A laughable moment... _____

A surprising moment... _____

An unforeseeable moment... _____

Wildlife spotted... _____

List

- [ ] _____
- [ ] _____
- [ ] _____
- [ ] _____
- [ ] _____
- [ ] _____
- [ ] _____
- [ ] _____
- [ ] _____
- [ ] _____
- [ ] _____
- [ ] _____
- [ ] _____
- [ ] _____
- [ ] _____
- [ ] _____
- [ ] _____

Snapped a selfie | Location...

Took a park sign photo? - ☐ y ☐ n

The weather was ...

PLAN YOUR TRIP:

☐ Day Trip   ☐ Overnight Stay

Reservations required: ☐ y ☐ n

Date reservations made: _____

Refund Policy: ☐ y ☐ n Site #: _____

Confirmation #: _____

Miles to travel: _____

Time traveling: _____

RV's?: ☐ y ☐ n Largest size RV? _____

Activities Accomplished:

☐ Archery	☐ Fishing	☐ Picknicking	☐ Walking
☐ Biking	☐ Hiking	☐ Rock Climbing	☐ Wildlife Watching
☐ Birding	☐ Horseback Riding	☐ Shooting Range	☐ _____
☐ Boating	☐ Hunting	☐ Snowshoeing	☐ _____
☐ Camping	☐ Off-Roading	☐ Stargazing	☐ _____
☐ Caving	☐ Paddle Boarding	☐ Swimming	☐ _____
☐ Geocaching	☐ Photography	☐ Tennis	☐ _____

Traveling by:

☐ ☐ ☐ ☐ ☐ ☐ ☐ ☐ ☐ ☐ ☐ ☐

RESERVATION INFORMATION:

Address: _____
_____

Reserved dates: _____

Check-in time: _____ Early check-in?: ☐ y ☐ n

Check-out time: _____ Late check-out?: ☐ y ☐ n

Website: _____

Phone: _____

WiFi: _____ WiFi password: _____

Dog friendly?: ☐ y ☐ n   Open all year?: ☐ y ☐ n

Add your favorite ticket stub, postcard, photo, stamp or drawing here

LET NEW ADVENTURES
» BEGIN →

Gaviota State Park

County: Santa Barbara

Established: 1953   *Acres: 2,787*

Flanks the narrow gorge of Gaviota Creek, which funnels Sundowner winds onto the popular beach area.

Star Rating
☆ ☆ ☆ ☆ ☆

My favorite thing about this place is... _____

Why I went ... _____

Who I went with ... _____

When I went ... _____

What I did... _____

What I saw... _____

What I learned... _____

An unforgettable moment... _____

A laughable moment... _____

A surprising moment... _____

An unforeseeable moment... _____

Wildlife spotted... _____

Snapped a selfie | Location... _____

Took a park sign photo? - ☐ y ☐ n

List
- ☐ _____
- ☐ _____
- ☐ _____
- ☐ _____
- ☐ _____
- ☐ _____
- ☐ _____
- ☐ _____
- ☐ _____
- ☐ _____
- ☐ _____
- ☐ _____
- ☐ _____
- ☐ _____
- ☐ _____
- ☐ _____
- ☐ _____
- ☐ _____
- ☐ _____
- ☐ _____

The weather was ... ☐ ☐ ☐ ☐ ☐ ☐ ☐

PLAN YOUR TRIP:

☐ Day Trip   ☐ Overnight Stay

Reservations required: ☐ y ☐ n

Date reservations made: _____

Refund Policy: ☐ y ☐ n   Site #: _____

Confirmation #: _____

Miles to travel: _____

Time traveling: _____

RV's?: ☐ y ☐ n Largest size RV? _____

Activities Accomplished:

☐ Archery
☐ Biking
☐ Birding
☐ Boating
☐ Camping
☐ Caving
☐ Geocaching

☐ Fishing
☐ Hiking
☐ Horseback Riding
☐ Hunting
☐ Off-Roading
☐ Paddle Boarding
☐ Photography

☐ Picknicking
☐ Rock Climbing
☐ Shooting Range
☐ Snowshoeing
☐ Stargazing
☐ Swimming
☐ Tennis

☐ Walking
☐ Wildlife Watching
☐ _____
☐ _____
☐ _____
☐ _____
☐ _____

Traveling by:

☐ ☐ ☐ ☐ ☐ ☐ ☐ ☐ ☐ ☐ ☐ ☐

RESERVATION INFORMATION:

Address: _____
_____

Reserved dates: _____

Check-in time: _____   Early check-in?: ☐ y ☐ n

Check-out time: _____   Late check-out?: ☐ y ☐ n

Website: _____

Phone: _____

WiFi: _____   WiFi password: _____

Dog friendly?: ☐ y ☐ n   Open all year?: ☐ y ☐ n

Add your favorite ticket stub, postcard, photo, stamp or drawing here

LET NEW ADVENTURES
>>> BEGIN →

GREAT VALLEY GRASSLANDS STATE PARK

County: Merced

Established: 1982

Acres: 2,826

Preserves a remnant of the native grasslands once extensive in the Central Valley.

Star Rating
☆ ☆ ☆ ☆ ☆

My favorite thing about this place is... _____

Why I went ... _____

Who I went with ... _____

When I went ... _____

What I did... _____

What I saw... _____

What I learned... _____

An unforgettable moment... _____

A laughable moment... _____

A surprising moment... _____

An unforeseeable moment... _____

Wildlife spotted... _____

List
- [ ] _____
- [ ] _____
- [ ] _____
- [ ] _____
- [ ] _____
- [ ] _____
- [ ] _____
- [ ] _____
- [ ] _____
- [ ] _____
- [ ] _____
- [ ] _____
- [ ] _____
- [ ] _____
- [ ] _____
- [ ] _____
- [ ] _____
- [ ] _____
- [ ] _____
- [ ] _____

📷 Snapped a selfie | Location...

📷 Took a park sign photo? - ☐ y ☐ n

The weather was ...
☐ ☐ ☐ ☐ ☐ ☐ ☐

PLAN YOUR TRIP:

☐ Day Trip   ☐ Overnight Stay

Reservations required: ☐y ☐n

Date reservations made: _____

Refund Policy: ☐y ☐n Site #: _____

Confirmation #: _____

Miles to travel: _____

Time traveling: _____

RV's?: ☐y ☐n Largest size RV? _____

Activities Accomplished:

☐ Archery
☐ Biking
☐ Birding
☐ Boating
☐ Camping
☐ Caving
☐ Geocaching

☐ Fishing
☐ Hiking
☐ Horseback Riding
☐ Hunting
☐ Off-Roading
☐ Paddle Boarding
☐ Photography

☐ Picknicking
☐ Rock Climbing
☐ Shooting Range
☐ Snowshoeing
☐ Stargazing
☐ Swimming
☐ Tennis

☐ Walking
☐ Wildlife Watching
☐ _____
☐ _____
☐ _____
☐ _____
☐ _____

RESERVATION INFORMATION:

Address: _____
_____

Reserved dates: _____

Check-in time: _____ Early check-in?: ☐y ☐n

Check-out time: _____ Late check-out?: ☐y ☐n

Website: _____

Phone: _____

WiFi: _____ WiFi password: _____

Dog friendly?: ☐y ☐n   Open all year?: ☐y ☐n

Traveling by:

☐ ☐ ☐ ☐ ☐ ☐ ☐ ☐ ☐ ☐ ☐ ☐

Add your favorite ticket stub, postcard, photo, stamp or drawing here

LET NEW ADVENTURES
»» BEGIN →

GRIZZLY CREEK REDWOODS STATE PARK

County: Humboldt

Established: 1943   Acres: 430

Harbors groves of coast redwoods in three separate units along the Van Duzen River.

Star Rating

☆ ☆ ☆ ☆ ☆

My favorite thing about this place is... _____

Why I went ... _____

Who I went with ... _____

When I went ... _____

What I did... _____

What I saw... _____

What I learned... _____

An unforgettable moment... _____

A laughable moment... _____

A surprising moment... _____

An unforeseeable moment... _____

Wildlife spotted... _____

📷 Snapped a selfie | Location... _____

📷 Took a park sign photo? - ☐ y ☐ n

List

☐ _____
☐ _____
☐ _____
☐ _____
☐ _____
☐ _____
☐ _____
☐ _____
☐ _____
☐ _____
☐ _____
☐ _____
☐ _____
☐ _____
☐ _____
☐ _____
☐ _____
☐ _____

The weather was ... ☐ ☐ ☐ ☐ ☐ ☐ ☐

PLAN YOUR TRIP:

☐ Day Trip   ☐ Overnight Stay

Reservations required: ☐ y ☐ n

Date reservations made: _____

Refund Policy: ☐ y ☐ n Site #: _____

Confirmation #: _____

Miles to travel: _____

Time traveling: _____

RV's?: ☐ y ☐ n Largest size RV? _____

Activities Accomplished:

☐ Archery
☐ Biking
☐ Birding
☐ Boating
☐ Camping
☐ Caving
☐ Geocaching

☐ Fishing
☐ Hiking
☐ Horseback Riding
☐ Hunting
☐ Off-Roading
☐ Paddle Boarding
☐ Photography

☐ Picknicking
☐ Rock Climbing
☐ Shooting Range
☐ Snowshoeing
☐ Stargazing
☐ Swimming
☐ Tennis

☐ Walking
☐ Wildlife Watching
☐ _____
☐ _____
☐ _____
☐ _____
☐ _____

RESERVATION INFORMATION:

Address: _____
_____

Reserved dates: _____

Check-in time: _____   Early check-in?: ☐ y ☐ n

Check-out time: _____   Late check-out?: ☐ y ☐ n

Website: _____

Phone: _____

WiFi: _____   WiFi password: _____

Dog friendly?: ☐ y ☐ n   Open all year?: ☐ y ☐ n

Traveling by:

☐ ☐ ☐ ☐ ☐ ☐ ☐ ☐ ☐ ☐ ☐ ☐

Add your favorite ticket stub, postcard, photo, stamp or drawing here

LET NEW ADVENTURES
≫ BEGIN →

Grover Hot Springs State Park

County: Alpine

Established: 1959

Acres: 553

Boasts hot springs that feed a swimming pool complex in an alpine meadow.

Star Rating
☆ ☆ ☆ ☆ ☆

My favorite thing about this place is... _____

Why I went ... _____

Who I went with ... _____

When I went ... _____

What I did... _____

What I saw... _____

What I learned... _____

An unforgettable moment... _____

A laughable moment... _____

A surprising moment... _____

An unforeseeable moment... _____

Wildlife spotted... _____

List
- [ ] _____
- [ ] _____
- [ ] _____
- [ ] _____
- [ ] _____
- [ ] _____
- [ ] _____
- [ ] _____
- [ ] _____
- [ ] _____
- [ ] _____
- [ ] _____
- [ ] _____
- [ ] _____
- [ ] _____
- [ ] _____
- [ ] _____
- [ ] _____
- [ ] _____

Snapped a selfie | Location... _____

Took a park sign photo? - ☐ y ☐ n

The weather was ... ☐ ☐ ☐ ☐ ☐ ☐ ☐

PLAN YOUR TRIP:

RESERVATION INFORMATION:

☐ Day Trip   ☐ Overnight Stay

Reservations required: ☐ y ☐ n

Date reservations made: _____

Refund Policy: ☐ y ☐ n Site #: _____

Confirmation #: _____

Miles to travel: _____

Time traveling: _____

RV's?: ☐ y ☐ n Largest size RV? _____

Address: _____
_____

Reserved dates: _____

Check-in time: _____ Early check-in?: ☐ y ☐ n

Check-out time: _____ Late check-out?: ☐ y ☐ n

Website: _____

Phone: _____

WiFi: _____ WiFi password: _____

Dog friendly?: ☐ y ☐ n   Open all year?: ☐ y ☐ n

Activities Accomplished:

☐ Archery
☐ Biking
☐ Birding
☐ Boating
☐ Camping
☐ Caving
☐ Geocaching

☐ Fishing
☐ Hiking
☐ Horseback Riding
☐ Hunting
☐ Off-Roading
☐ Paddle Boarding
☐ Photography

☐ Picknicking
☐ Rock Climbing
☐ Shooting Range
☐ Snowshoeing
☐ Stargazing
☐ Swimming
☐ Tennis

☐ Walking
☐ Wildlife Watching
☐ _____
☐ _____
☐ _____
☐ _____
☐ _____

Traveling by:

☐ ☐ ☐ ☐ ☐ ☐ ☐ ☐ ☐ ☐ ☐ ☐

Add your favorite ticket stub, postcard, photo, stamp or drawing here

LET NEW ADVENTURES
»» BEGIN →

Harmony Headlands State Park

County: San Luis Obispo

Established: 2003   *Acres: 748*

Preserves an undeveloped parcel of Pacific coast.

Star Rating

☆ ☆ ☆ ☆ ☆

My favorite thing about this place is... _____

Why I went ... _____

Who I went with ... _____

When I went ... _____

What I did... _____

What I saw... _____

What I learned... _____

An unforgettable moment... _____

A laughable moment... _____

A surprising moment... _____

An unforeseeable moment... _____

Wildlife spotted... _____

List
- ☐ _____
- ☐ _____
- ☐ _____
- ☐ _____
- ☐ _____
- ☐ _____
- ☐ _____
- ☐ _____
- ☐ _____
- ☐ _____
- ☐ _____
- ☐ _____
- ☐ _____
- ☐ _____
- ☐ _____
- ☐ _____
- ☐ _____
- ☐ _____

Snapped a selfie | Location... _____

Took a park sign photo? - ☐ y ☐ n

The weather was ...   ☐ ☐ ☐ ☐ ☐ ☐ ☐

PLAN YOUR TRIP:

☐ Day Trip   ☐ Overnight Stay

Reservations required: ☐ y ☐ n

Date reservations made: _____

Refund Policy: ☐ y ☐ n Site #: _____

Confirmation #: _____

Miles to travel: _____

Time traveling: _____

RV's?: ☐ y ☐ n Largest size RV? _____

Activities Accomplished:

☐ Archery   ☐ Fishing   ☐ Picknicking   ☐ Walking
☐ Biking   ☐ Hiking   ☐ Rock Climbing   ☐ Wildlife Watching
☐ Birding   ☐ Horseback Riding ☐ Shooting Range   ☐ _____
☐ Boating   ☐ Hunting   ☐ Snowshoeing   ☐ _____
☐ Camping   ☐ Off-Roading   ☐ Stargazing   ☐ _____
☐ Caving   ☐ Paddle Boarding ☐ Swimming   ☐ _____
☐ Geocaching   ☐ Photography   ☐ Tennis   ☐ _____

Traveling by:

☐   ☐   ☐   ☐   ☐   ☐   ☐   ☐   ☐   ☐   ☐   ☐

RESERVATION INFORMATION:

Address: _____
_____

Reserved dates: _____

Check-in time: _____   Early check-in?: ☐ y ☐ n

Check-out time: _____   Late check-out?: ☐ y ☐ n

Website: _____

Phone: _____

WiFi: _____   WiFi password: _____

Dog friendly?: ☐ y ☐ n   Open all year?: ☐ y ☐ n

Add your favorite ticket stub, postcard, photo, stamp or drawing here

LET NEW ADVENTURES
≫ BEGIN →

HEARST SAN SIMEON STATE PARK

County: San Luis Obispo

Established: 1932   *Acres: 2,309*

Preserves rocky coast and rare habitats like mima mounds and Monterey pine forest, as well as a 5,850-year-old Native American archaeological site.

Star Rating
☆ ☆ ☆ ☆ ☆

My favorite thing about this place is... _____

Why I went ... _____

Who I went with ... _____

When I went ... _____

What I did... _____

What I saw... _____

What I learned... _____

An unforgettable moment... _____

A laughable moment... _____

A surprising moment... _____

An unforeseeable moment... _____

Wildlife spotted... _____

Snapped a selfie | Location... _____

Took a park sign photo? - ☐ y ☐ n

List
- ☐ _____
- ☐ _____
- ☐ _____
- ☐ _____
- ☐ _____
- ☐ _____
- ☐ _____
- ☐ _____
- ☐ _____
- ☐ _____
- ☐ _____
- ☐ _____
- ☐ _____
- ☐ _____
- ☐ _____
- ☐ _____
- ☐ _____
- ☐ _____
- ☐ _____
- ☐ _____

The weather was ...
☐ ☐ ☐ ☐ ☐ ☐ ☐

PLAN YOUR TRIP:

☐ Day Trip   ☐ Overnight Stay

Reservations required: ☐ y ☐ n

Date reservations made: _____

Refund Policy: ☐ y ☐ n Site #: _____

Confirmation #: _____

Miles to travel: _____

Time traveling: _____

RV's?: ☐ y ☐ n Largest size RV? _____

Activities Accomplished:

RESERVATION INFORMATION:

Address: _____
_____

Reserved dates: _____

Check-in time: _____ Early check-in?: ☐ y ☐ n

Check-out time: _____ Late check-out?: ☐ y ☐ n

Website: _____

Phone: _____

WiFi: _____ WiFi password: _____

Dog friendly?: ☐ y ☐ n   Open all year?: ☐ y ☐ n

☐ Archery	☐ Fishing	☐ Picknicking	☐ Walking
☐ Biking	☐ Hiking	☐ Rock Climbing	☐ Wildlife Watching
☐ Birding	☐ Horseback Riding	☐ Shooting Range	☐ _____
☐ Boating	☐ Hunting	☐ Snowshoeing	☐ _____
☐ Camping	☐ Off-Roading	☐ Stargazing	☐ _____
☐ Caving	☐ Paddle Boarding	☐ Swimming	☐ _____
☐ Geocaching	☐ Photography	☐ Tennis	☐ _____

Traveling by:

☐ ☐ ☐ ☐ ☐ ☐ ☐ ☐ ☐ ☐ ☐ ☐

Add your favorite ticket stub, postcard, photo, stamp or drawing here

LET NEW ADVENTURES
≫ BEGIN →

Hendy Woods State Park

County: Mendocino

Established: 1958

Acres: 816

Preserves two groves of old-growth coast redwoods in the Anderson Valley.

Star Rating
☆ ☆ ☆ ☆ ☆

My favorite thing about this place is... _____

Why I went ... _____

Who I went with ... _____

When I went ... _____

What I did... _____

What I saw... _____

What I learned... _____

An unforgettable moment... _____

A laughable moment... _____

A surprising moment... _____

An unforeseeable moment... _____

Wildlife spotted... _____

List

☐ _____
☐ _____
☐ _____
☐ _____
☐ _____
☐ _____
☐ _____
☐ _____
☐ _____
☐ _____
☐ _____
☐ _____
☐ _____
☐ _____
☐ _____
☐ _____

Snapped a selfie | Location... _____

Took a park sign photo? - ☐ y ☐ n

The weather was ...
☐ ☐ ☐ ☐ ☐ ☐ ☐

PLAN YOUR TRIP:

☐ Day Trip   ☐ Overnight Stay

Reservations required: ☐ y ☐ n

Date reservations made: _____

Refund Policy: ☐ y ☐ n Site #: _____

Confirmation #: _____

Miles to travel: _____

Time traveling: _____

RV's?: ☐ y ☐ n Largest size RV? _____

Activities Accomplished:

☐ Archery
☐ Biking
☐ Birding
☐ Boating
☐ Camping
☐ Caving
☐ Geocaching

☐ Fishing
☐ Hiking
☐ Horseback Riding
☐ Hunting
☐ Off-Roading
☐ Paddle Boarding
☐ Photography

☐ Picknicking
☐ Rock Climbing
☐ Shooting Range
☐ Snowshoeing
☐ Stargazing
☐ Swimming
☐ Tennis

☐ Walking
☐ Wildlife Watching
☐ _____
☐ _____
☐ _____
☐ _____
☐ _____

Traveling by:

☐ ☐ ☐ ☐ ☐ ☐ ☐ ☐ ☐ ☐ ☐ ☐

RESERVATION INFORMATION:

Address: _____
_____

Reserved dates: _____

Check-in time: _____ Early check-in?: ☐ y ☐ n

Check-out time: _____ Late check-out?: ☐ y ☐ n

Website: _____

Phone: _____

WiFi: _____ WiFi password: _____

Dog friendly?: ☐ y ☐ n   Open all year?: ☐ y ☐ n

Add your favorite ticket stub, postcard, photo, stamp or drawing here

LET NEW ADVENTURES
≫ BEGIN →

Henry Cowell Redwoods State Park

County: Santa Cruz

Established: 1953

Acres: 4,623

Boasts its Redwood Grove and other old-growth forest.

Star Rating

☆ ☆ ☆ ☆ ☆

My favorite thing about this place is... _____

Why I went ... _____

Who I went with ... _____

When I went ... _____

What I did... _____

What I saw... _____

What I learned... _____

An unforgettable moment... _____

A laughable moment... _____

A surprising moment... _____

An unforeseeable moment... _____

Wildlife spotted... _____

List

☐ _____
☐ _____
☐ _____
☐ _____
☐ _____
☐ _____
☐ _____
☐ _____
☐ _____
☐ _____
☐ _____
☐ _____
☐ _____
☐ _____
☐ _____
☐ _____
☐ _____
☐ _____
☐ _____

📷 Snapped a selfie | Location... _____

📷 Took a park sign photo? - ☐ y ☐ n

The weather was ...

☐ ☐ ☐ ☐ ☐ ☐ ☐

PLAN YOUR TRIP:

RESERVATION INFORMATION:

☐ Day Trip   ☐ Overnight Stay

Reservations required: ☐y ☐n

Date reservations made: _____

Refund Policy: ☐y ☐n Site #: _____

Confirmation #: _____

Miles to travel: _____

Time traveling: _____

RV's?: ☐y ☐n Largest size RV? _____

Address: _____
_____

Reserved dates: _____

Check-in time: _____ Early check-in?: ☐y ☐n

Check-out time: _____ Late check-out?: ☐y ☐n

Website: _____

Phone: _____

WiFi: _____ WiFi password: _____

Dog friendly?: ☐y ☐n   Open all year?: ☐y ☐n

Activities Accomplished:

☐ Archery
☐ Biking
☐ Birding
☐ Boating
☐ Camping
☐ Caving
☐ Geocaching

☐ Fishing
☐ Hiking
☐ Horseback Riding
☐ Hunting
☐ Off-Roading
☐ Paddle Boarding
☐ Photography

☐ Picknicking
☐ Rock Climbing
☐ Shooting Range
☐ Snowshoeing
☐ Stargazing
☐ Swimming
☐ Tennis

☐ Walking
☐ Wildlife Watching
☐ _____
☐ _____
☐ _____
☐ _____
☐ _____

Traveling by:

☐ ☐ ☐ ☐ ☐ ☐ ☐ ☐ ☐ ☐ ☐ ☐

Add your favorite ticket stub, postcard, photo, stamp or drawing here

LET NEW ADVENTURES
≫ BEGIN →

Henry W. Coe State Park

County: Santa Clara and Stanislaus

Established: 1959　　　　　　　　　　　　　　　　　　　　　　*Acres: 89,164*

Encompasses a sprawling wilderness of ridges and steep canyons in the Diablo Range.

Star Rating
☆ ☆ ☆ ☆ ☆

My favorite thing about this place is... _____

Why I went ... _____

Who I went with ... _____

When I went ... _____

What I did... _____

What I saw... _____

What I learned... _____

An unforgettable moment... _____

A laughable moment... _____

A surprising moment... _____

An unforeseeable moment... _____

Wildlife spotted... _____

List
- [ ] _____
- [ ] _____
- [ ] _____
- [ ] _____
- [ ] _____
- [ ] _____
- [ ] _____
- [ ] _____
- [ ] _____
- [ ] _____
- [ ] _____
- [ ] _____
- [ ] _____
- [ ] _____
- [ ] _____
- [ ] _____
- [ ] _____
- [ ] _____

Snapped a selfie | Location... _____

Took a park sign photo? - ☐ y ☐ n

The weather was ...　☐　☐　☐　☐　☐　☐　☐

PLAN YOUR TRIP:

☐ Day Trip   ☐ Overnight Stay

Reservations required: ☐ y ☐ n

Date reservations made: _____

Refund Policy: ☐ y ☐ n Site #: _____

Confirmation #: _____

Miles to travel: _____

Time traveling: _____

RV's?: ☐ y ☐ n Largest size RV? _____

Activities Accomplished:

☐ Archery
☐ Biking
☐ Birding
☐ Boating
☐ Camping
☐ Caving
☐ Geocaching

☐ Fishing
☐ Hiking
☐ Horseback Riding
☐ Hunting
☐ Off-Roading
☐ Paddle Boarding
☐ Photography

☐ Picknicking
☐ Rock Climbing
☐ Shooting Range
☐ Snowshoeing
☐ Stargazing
☐ Swimming
☐ Tennis

☐ Walking
☐ Wildlife Watching
☐ _____
☐ _____
☐ _____
☐ _____
☐ _____

RESERVATION INFORMATION:

Address: _____
_____

Reserved dates: _____

Check-in time: _____   Early check-in?: ☐ y ☐ n

Check-out time: _____   Late check-out?: ☐ y ☐ n

Website: _____

Phone: _____

WiFi: _____   WiFi password: _____

Dog friendly?: ☐ y ☐ n   Open all year?: ☐ y ☐ n

Traveling by:

☐ ☐ ☐ ☐ ☐ ☐ ☐ ☐ ☐ ☐ ☐ ☐

Add your favorite ticket stub, postcard, photo, stamp or drawing here

LET NEW ADVENTURES
≫ BEGIN →

Humboldt Lagoons State Park

County: Humboldt

Established: 1931

Acres: 2,256

Protects part of the largest lagoon system in the United States, including Big Lagoon, Stone Lagoon, and Freshwater Lagoon.

Star Rating
☆☆☆☆☆

My favorite thing about this place is... _____

Why I went ... _____

Who I went with ... _____

When I went ... _____

What I did... _____

What I saw... _____

What I learned... _____

An unforgettable moment... _____

A laughable moment... _____

A surprising moment... _____

An unforeseeable moment... _____

Wildlife spotted... _____

List

- [ ] _____
- [ ] _____
- [ ] _____
- [ ] _____
- [ ] _____
- [ ] _____
- [ ] _____
- [ ] _____
- [ ] _____
- [ ] _____
- [ ] _____
- [ ] _____
- [ ] _____
- [ ] _____
- [ ] _____
- [ ] _____
- [ ] _____
- [ ] _____

Snapped a selfie | Location... _____

Took a park sign photo? - ☐ y ☐ n

The weather was ...
☐ ☐ ☐ ☐ ☐ ☐ ☐

PLAN YOUR TRIP:

RESERVATION INFORMATION:

☐ Day Trip   ☐ Overnight Stay

Reservations required: ☐ y ☐ n

Date reservations made: _____

Refund Policy: ☐ y ☐ n Site #: _____

Confirmation #: _____

Miles to travel: _____

Time traveling: _____

RV's?: ☐ y ☐ n Largest size RV? _____

Address: _____
_____

Reserved dates: _____

Check-in time: _____ Early check-in?: ☐ y ☐ n

Check-out time: _____ Late check-out?: ☐ y ☐ n

Website: _____

Phone: _____

WiFi: _____ WiFi password: _____

Dog friendly?: ☐ y ☐ n   Open all year?: ☐ y ☐ n

Activities Accomplished:

☐ Archery
☐ Biking
☐ Birding
☐ Boating
☐ Camping
☐ Caving
☐ Geocaching

☐ Fishing
☐ Hiking
☐ Horseback Riding
☐ Hunting
☐ Off-Roading
☐ Paddle Boarding
☐ Photography

☐ Picknicking
☐ Rock Climbing
☐ Shooting Range
☐ Snowshoeing
☐ Stargazing
☐ Swimming
☐ Tennis

☐ Walking
☐ Wildlife Watching
☐ _____
☐ _____
☐ _____
☐ _____
☐ _____

Traveling by:

☐   ☐   ☐   ☐   ☐   ☐   ☐   ☐   ☐   ☐   ☐   ☐

Add your favorite ticket stub, postcard, photo, stamp or drawing here

LET NEW ADVENTURES
≫ BEGIN →

Humboldt Redwoods State Park

County: Humboldt

Established: 1921   *Acres: 51,651*

Preserves the world's largest remaining old-growth coast redwood forest, including Stratosphere Giant, the fourth-tallest known tree.

Star Rating
☆ ☆ ☆ ☆ ☆

My favorite thing about this place is... _____

Why I went ... _____

Who I went with ... _____

When I went ... _____

What I did... _____

What I saw... _____

What I learned... _____

An unforgettable moment... _____

A laughable moment... _____

A surprising moment... _____

An unforeseeable moment... _____

Wildlife spotted... _____

List
- ☐ _____
- ☐ _____
- ☐ _____
- ☐ _____
- ☐ _____
- ☐ _____
- ☐ _____
- ☐ _____
- ☐ _____
- ☐ _____
- ☐ _____
- ☐ _____
- ☐ _____
- ☐ _____
- ☐ _____
- ☐ _____
- ☐ _____

Snapped a selfie | Location... _____

Took a park sign photo? - ☐ y ☐ n

The weather was ...
☐ ☐ ☐ ☐ ☐ ☐ ☐

PLAN YOUR TRIP:

RESERVATION INFORMATION:

☐ Day Trip   ☐ Overnight Stay

Reservations required: ☐ y ☐ n

Date reservations made: _____

Refund Policy: ☐ y ☐ n Site #: _____

Confirmation #: _____

Miles to travel: _____

Time traveling: _____

RV's?: ☐ y ☐ n Largest size RV? _____

Address: _____
_____

Reserved dates: _____

Check-in time: _____ Early check-in?: ☐ y ☐ n

Check-out time: _____ Late check-out?: ☐ y ☐ n

Website: _____

Phone: _____

WiFi: _____ WiFi password: _____

Dog friendly?: ☐ y ☐ n   Open all year?: ☐ y ☐ n

Activities Accomplished:

☐ Archery
☐ Biking
☐ Birding
☐ Boating
☐ Camping
☐ Caving
☐ Geocaching

☐ Fishing
☐ Hiking
☐ Horseback Riding
☐ Hunting
☐ Off-Roading
☐ Paddle Boarding
☐ Photography

☐ Picknicking
☐ Rock Climbing
☐ Shooting Range
☐ Snowshoeing
☐ Stargazing
☐ Swimming
☐ Tennis

☐ Walking
☐ Wildlife Watching
☐ _____
☐ _____
☐ _____
☐ _____
☐ _____

Traveling by:

☐ ☐ ☐ ☐ ☐ ☐ ☐ ☐ ☐ ☐ ☐ ☐

Add your favorite ticket stub, postcard, photo, stamp or drawing here

LET NEW ADVENTURES
»» BEGIN →

Jedediah Smith Redwoods State Park

County: Del Norte

Established: 1939

Acres: 10,430

Honors explorer Jedediah Smith with a tract of coast redwoods along the Smith River. Part of Redwood National and State Parks.

Star Rating
☆ ☆ ☆ ☆ ☆

My favorite thing about this place is... _____

Why I went ... _____

Who I went with ... _____

When I went ... _____

What I did... _____

What I saw... _____

What I learned... _____

An unforgettable moment... _____

A laughable moment... _____

A surprising moment... _____

An unforeseeable moment... _____

Wildlife spotted... _____

List
☐ _____
☐ _____
☐ _____
☐ _____
☐ _____
☐ _____
☐ _____
☐ _____
☐ _____
☐ _____
☐ _____
☐ _____
☐ _____
☐ _____
☐ _____
☐ _____
☐ _____
☐ _____
☐ _____
☐ _____
☐ _____

📷 Snapped a selfie | Location... _____

📷 Took a park sign photo? - ☐ y ☐ n

The weather was ...
☐ ☐ ☐ ☐ ☐ ☐ ☐

PLAN YOUR TRIP:

☐ Day Trip   ☐ Overnight Stay

Reservations required: ☐ y ☐ n

Date reservations made: _____

Refund Policy: ☐ y ☐ n Site #: _____

Confirmation #: _____

Miles to travel: _____

Time traveling: _____

RV's?: ☐ y ☐ n Largest size RV? _____

Activities Accomplished:

☐ Archery   ☐ Fishing   ☐ Picknicking   ☐ Walking
☐ Biking   ☐ Hiking   ☐ Rock Climbing   ☐ Wildlife Watching
☐ Birding   ☐ Horseback Riding   ☐ Shooting Range   ☐ _____
☐ Boating   ☐ Hunting   ☐ Snowshoeing   ☐ _____
☐ Camping   ☐ Off-Roading   ☐ Stargazing   ☐ _____
☐ Caving   ☐ Paddle Boarding   ☐ Swimming   ☐ _____
☐ Geocaching   ☐ Photography   ☐ Tennis   ☐ _____

Traveling by:

☐   ☐   ☐   ☐   ☐   ☐   ☐   ☐   ☐   ☐   ☐   ☐

RESERVATION INFORMATION:

Address: _____
_____

Reserved dates: _____

Check-in time: _____   Early check-in?: ☐ y ☐ n

Check-out time: _____   Late check-out?: ☐ y ☐ n

Website: _____

Phone: _____

WiFi: _____ WiFi password: _____

Dog friendly?: ☐ y ☐ n   Open all year?: ☐ y ☐ n

Add your favorite ticket stub, postcard, photo, stamp or drawing here

LET NEW ADVENTURES
»» BEGIN →

Julia Pfeiffer Burns State Park

County: Monterey

Established: *1962*   *Acres: 3,762*

Stretches from the Big Sur coast up to 3,000-foot (910 m) ridges. Includes the iconic seaside McWay Falls.

Star Rating
☆☆☆☆☆

My favorite thing about this place is... _____

Why I went ... _____

Who I went with ... _____

When I went ... _____

What I did... _____

What I saw... _____

What I learned... _____

An unforgettable moment... _____

A laughable moment... _____

A surprising moment... _____

An unforeseeable moment... _____

Wildlife spotted... _____

 Snapped a selfie | Location... _____

 Took a park sign photo? - ☐ y ☐ n

List
- ☐ _____
- ☐ _____
- ☐ _____
- ☐ _____
- ☐ _____
- ☐ _____
- ☐ _____
- ☐ _____
- ☐ _____
- ☐ _____
- ☐ _____
- ☐ _____
- ☐ _____
- ☐ _____
- ☐ _____
- ☐ _____
- ☐ _____
- ☐ _____
- ☐ _____
- ☐ _____

The weather was ...

☐   ☐   ☐   ☐   ☐   ☐   ☐

PLAN YOUR TRIP:

☐ Day Trip   ☐ Overnight Stay

Reservations required: ☐y ☐n

Date reservations made: _____

Refund Policy: ☐y ☐n Site #: _____

Confirmation #: _____

Miles to travel: _____

Time traveling: _____

RV's?: ☐y ☐n Largest size RV? _____

Activities Accomplished:

☐ Archery
☐ Biking
☐ Birding
☐ Boating
☐ Camping
☐ Caving
☐ Geocaching

☐ Fishing
☐ Hiking
☐ Horseback Riding
☐ Hunting
☐ Off-Roading
☐ Paddle Boarding
☐ Photography

☐ Picknicking
☐ Rock Climbing
☐ Shooting Range
☐ Snowshoeing
☐ Stargazing
☐ Swimming
☐ Tennis

☐ Walking
☐ Wildlife Watching
☐ _____
☐ _____
☐ _____
☐ _____
☐ _____

Traveling by:

☐ ☐ ☐ ☐ ☐ ☐ ☐ ☐ ☐ ☐ ☐ ☐

RESERVATION INFORMATION:

Address: _____
_____

Reserved dates: _____

Check-in time: _____ Early check-in?: ☐y ☐n

Check-out time: _____ Late check-out?: ☐y ☐n

Website: _____

Phone: _____

WiFi: _____ WiFi password: _____

Dog friendly?: ☐y ☐n   Open all year?: ☐y ☐n

Add your favorite ticket stub, postcard, photo, stamp or drawing here

LET NEW ADVENTURES
≫ BEGIN →

LEO CARRILLO STATE PARK

County: Los Angeles and Ventura

Established: 1953   Acres: 2,513

Honors actor and conservationist Leo Carrillo with a 1.5-mile (2.4 km) beach. Part of Santa Monica Mountains National Recreation Area.

Star Rating
☆ ☆ ☆ ☆ ☆

My favorite thing about this place is... _____

Why I went ... _____

Who I went with ... _____

When I went ... _____

What I did... _____

What I saw... _____

What I learned... _____

An unforgettable moment... _____

A laughable moment... _____

A surprising moment... _____

An unforeseeable moment... _____

Wildlife spotted... _____

List
- [ ] _____
- [ ] _____
- [ ] _____
- [ ] _____
- [ ] _____
- [ ] _____
- [ ] _____
- [ ] _____
- [ ] _____
- [ ] _____
- [ ] _____
- [ ] _____
- [ ] _____
- [ ] _____
- [ ] _____
- [ ] _____
- [ ] _____
- [ ] _____
- [ ] _____

Snapped a selfie | Location... _____

Took a park sign photo? - ☐ y ☐ n

The weather was ...   ☐ ☐ ☐ ☐ ☐ ☐ ☐

PLAN YOUR TRIP:

☐ Day Trip   ☐ Overnight Stay

Reservations required: ☐ y ☐ n

Date reservations made: _____

Refund Policy: ☐ y ☐ n   Site #: _____

Confirmation #: _____

Miles to travel: _____

Time traveling: _____

RV's?: ☐ y ☐ n Largest size RV? _____

Activities Accomplished:

☐ Archery
☐ Biking
☐ Birding
☐ Boating
☐ Camping
☐ Caving
☐ Geocaching

☐ Fishing
☐ Hiking
☐ Horseback Riding
☐ Hunting
☐ Off-Roading
☐ Paddle Boarding
☐ Photography

☐ Picknicking
☐ Rock Climbing
☐ Shooting Range
☐ Snowshoeing
☐ Stargazing
☐ Swimming
☐ Tennis

☐ Walking
☐ Wildlife Watching
☐ _____
☐ _____
☐ _____
☐ _____
☐ _____

RESERVATION INFORMATION:

Address: _____
_____

Reserved dates: _____

Check-in time: _____   Early check-in?: ☐ y ☐ n

Check-out time: _____   Late check-out?: ☐ y ☐ n

Website: _____

Phone: _____

WiFi: _____   WiFi password: _____

Dog friendly?: ☐ y ☐ n   Open all year?: ☐ y ☐ n

Traveling by:

☐ ☐ ☐ ☐ ☐ ☐ ☐ ☐ ☐ ☐ ☐ ☐

Add your favorite ticket stub, postcard, photo, stamp or drawing here

LET NEW ADVENTURES
≫ BEGIN →

Limekiln State Park

County: Monterey

Established: 1994

Acres: 711

Contains four lime kilns from an 1887 lime-smelting operation on the Big Sur coast.

Star Rating
☆ ☆ ☆ ☆ ☆

My favorite thing about this place is... _____

Why I went ... _____

Who I went with ... _____

When I went ... _____

What I did... _____

What I saw... _____

What I learned... _____

An unforgettable moment... _____

A laughable moment... _____

A surprising moment... _____

An unforeseeable moment... _____

Wildlife spotted... _____

List
- [ ] _____
- [ ] _____
- [ ] _____
- [ ] _____
- [ ] _____
- [ ] _____
- [ ] _____
- [ ] _____
- [ ] _____
- [ ] _____
- [ ] _____
- [ ] _____
- [ ] _____
- [ ] _____
- [ ] _____
- [ ] _____
- [ ] _____
- [ ] _____
- [ ] _____

Snapped a selfie | Location... _____

Took a park sign photo? - ☐ y ☐ n

The weather was ... ☐ ☐ ☐ ☐ ☐ ☐ ☐

PLAN YOUR TRIP:

☐ Day Trip   ☐ Overnight Stay

Reservations required: ☐ y ☐ n

Date reservations made: _____

Refund Policy: ☐ y ☐ n   Site #: _____

Confirmation #: _____

Miles to travel: _____

Time traveling: _____

RV's?: ☐ y ☐ n Largest size RV? _____

Activities Accomplished:

☐ Archery
☐ Biking
☐ Birding
☐ Boating
☐ Camping
☐ Caving
☐ Geocaching

☐ Fishing
☐ Hiking
☐ Horseback Riding
☐ Hunting
☐ Off-Roading
☐ Paddle Boarding
☐ Photography

☐ Picknicking
☐ Rock Climbing
☐ Shooting Range
☐ Snowshoeing
☐ Stargazing
☐ Swimming
☐ Tennis

☐ Walking
☐ Wildlife Watching
☐ _____
☐ _____
☐ _____
☐ _____
☐ _____

RESERVATION INFORMATION:

Address: _____
_____

Reserved dates: _____

Check-in time: _____   Early check-in?: ☐ y ☐ n

Check-out time: _____   Late check-out?: ☐ y ☐ n

Website: _____

Phone: _____

WiFi: _____   WiFi password: _____

Dog friendly?: ☐ y ☐ n   Open all year?: ☐ y ☐ n

Traveling by:

☐ ☐ ☐ ☐ ☐ ☐ ☐ ☐ ☐ ☐ ☐ ☐

Add your favorite ticket stub, postcard, photo, stamp or drawing here

LET NEW ADVENTURES
≫ BEGIN →

MacKerricher State Park

County: Mendocino

Established: 1949   *Acres:* 2,519

Star Rating
☆☆☆☆☆

My favorite thing about this place is... _____

Why I went ... _____

Who I went with ... _____

When I went ... _____

What I did... _____

What I saw... _____

What I learned... _____

An unforgettable moment... _____

A laughable moment... _____

A surprising moment... _____

An unforeseeable moment... _____

Wildlife spotted... _____

List

- [ ] _____
- [ ] _____
- [ ] _____
- [ ] _____
- [ ] _____
- [ ] _____
- [ ] _____
- [ ] _____
- [ ] _____
- [ ] _____
- [ ] _____
- [ ] _____
- [ ] _____
- [ ] _____
- [ ] _____
- [ ] _____
- [ ] _____
- [ ] _____
- [ ] _____

📷 Snapped a selfie | Location...

📷 Took a park sign photo? - ☐ y ☐ n

The weather was ...   ☐ ☐ ☐ ☐ ☐ ☐ ☐

PLAN YOUR TRIP:

☐ Day Trip   ☐ Overnight Stay

Reservations required: ☐y ☐n

Date reservations made: _____

Refund Policy: ☐y ☐n Site #: _____

Confirmation #: _____

Miles to travel: _____

Time traveling: _____

RV's?: ☐y ☐n Largest size RV? _____

Activities Accomplished:

☐ Archery
☐ Biking
☐ Birding
☐ Boating
☐ Camping
☐ Caving
☐ Geocaching

☐ Fishing
☐ Hiking
☐ Horseback Riding
☐ Hunting
☐ Off-Roading
☐ Paddle Boarding
☐ Photography

☐ Picknicking
☐ Rock Climbing
☐ Shooting Range
☐ Snowshoeing
☐ Stargazing
☐ Swimming
☐ Tennis

☐ Walking
☐ Wildlife Watching
☐ _____
☐ _____
☐ _____
☐ _____
☐ _____

Traveling by:

☐ ☐ ☐ ☐ ☐ ☐ ☐ ☐ ☐ ☐ ☐ ☐

RESERVATION INFORMATION:

Address: _____
_____

Reserved dates: _____

Check-in time: _____ Early check-in?: ☐y ☐n

Check-out time: _____ Late check-out?: ☐y ☐n

Website: _____

Phone: _____

WiFi: _____ WiFi password: _____

Dog friendly?: ☐y ☐n   Open all year?: ☐y ☐n

Add your favorite ticket stub, postcard, photo, stamp or drawing here

LET NEW ADVENTURES
»» BEGIN →

Malibu Creek State Park

County: Los Angeles

Established: 1974

Acres: 8,215

Star Rating
☆ ☆ ☆ ☆ ☆

My favorite thing about this place is... _____

Why I went ... _____

Who I went with ... _____

When I went ... _____

What I did... _____

What I saw... _____

What I learned... _____

An unforgettable moment... _____

A laughable moment... _____

A surprising moment... _____

An unforeseeable moment... _____

Wildlife spotted... _____

List
- [ ] _____
- [ ] _____
- [ ] _____
- [ ] _____
- [ ] _____
- [ ] _____
- [ ] _____
- [ ] _____
- [ ] _____
- [ ] _____
- [ ] _____
- [ ] _____
- [ ] _____
- [ ] _____
- [ ] _____
- [ ] _____
- [ ] _____
- [ ] _____

Snapped a selfie | Location... _____

Took a park sign photo? - ☐ y ☐ n

The weather was ...
☐ ☐ ☐ ☐ ☐ ☐ ☐

PLAN YOUR TRIP:

☐ Day Trip   ☐ Overnight Stay

Reservations required: ☐ y ☐ n

Date reservations made: _____

Refund Policy: ☐ y ☐ n   Site #: _____

Confirmation #: _____

Miles to travel: _____

Time traveling: _____

RV's?: ☐ y ☐ n Largest size RV? _____

Activities Accomplished:

☐ Archery
☐ Biking
☐ Birding
☐ Boating
☐ Camping
☐ Caving
☐ Geocaching

☐ Fishing
☐ Hiking
☐ Horseback Riding
☐ Hunting
☐ Off-Roading
☐ Paddle Boarding
☐ Photography

☐ Picknicking
☐ Rock Climbing
☐ Shooting Range
☐ Snowshoeing
☐ Stargazing
☐ Swimming
☐ Tennis

☐ Walking
☐ Wildlife Watching
☐ _____
☐ _____
☐ _____
☐ _____
☐ _____

RESERVATION INFORMATION:

Address: _____
_____

Reserved dates: _____

Check-in time: _____   Early check-in?: ☐ y ☐ n

Check-out time: _____   Late check-out?: ☐ y ☐ n

Website: _____

Phone: _____

WiFi: _____   WiFi password: _____

Dog friendly?: ☐ y ☐ n   Open all year?: ☐ y ☐ n

Traveling by:

☐ ☐ ☐ ☐ ☐ ☐ ☐ ☐ ☐ ☐ ☐ ☐

Add your favorite ticket stub, postcard, photo, stamp or drawing here

LET NEW ADVENTURES
≫ BEGIN →

MANCHESTER STATE PARK

County: Mendocino

Established: 1955

Acres: 5,272

Star Rating
☆ ☆ ☆ ☆ ☆

My favorite thing about this place is... _____

Why I went ... _____

Who I went with ... _____

When I went ... _____

What I did... _____

What I saw... _____

What I learned... _____

An unforgettable moment... _____

A laughable moment... _____

A surprising moment... _____

An unforeseeable moment... _____

Wildlife spotted... _____

Snapped a selfie | Location... _____

Took a park sign photo? - ☐ y ☐ n

List
- ☐ _____
- ☐ _____
- ☐ _____
- ☐ _____
- ☐ _____
- ☐ _____
- ☐ _____
- ☐ _____
- ☐ _____
- ☐ _____
- ☐ _____
- ☐ _____
- ☐ _____
- ☐ _____
- ☐ _____
- ☐ _____
- ☐ _____
- ☐ _____

The weather was ...
☐ ☐ ☐ ☐ ☐ ☐ ☐

PLAN YOUR TRIP:

☐ Day Trip   ☐ Overnight Stay

Reservations required: ☐ y ☐ n

Date reservations made: _____

Refund Policy: ☐ y ☐ n Site #: _____

Confirmation #: _____

Miles to travel: _____

Time traveling: _____

RV's?: ☐ y ☐ n Largest size RV? _____

Activities Accomplished:

☐ Archery
☐ Biking
☐ Birding
☐ Boating
☐ Camping
☐ Caving
☐ Geocaching

☐ Fishing
☐ Hiking
☐ Horseback Riding
☐ Hunting
☐ Off-Roading
☐ Paddle Boarding
☐ Photography

☐ Picknicking
☐ Rock Climbing
☐ Shooting Range
☐ Snowshoeing
☐ Stargazing
☐ Swimming
☐ Tennis

☐ Walking
☐ Wildlife Watching
☐ _____
☐ _____
☐ _____
☐ _____
☐ _____

Traveling by:

☐   ☐   ☐   ☐   ☐   ☐   ☐   ☐   ☐   ☐   ☐   ☐

RESERVATION INFORMATION:

Address: _____
_____

Reserved dates: _____

Check-in time: _____   Early check-in?: ☐ y ☐ n

Check-out time: _____   Late check-out?: ☐ y ☐ n

Website: _____

Phone: _____

WiFi: _____   WiFi password: _____

Dog friendly?: ☐ y ☐ n   Open all year?: ☐ y ☐ n

Add your favorite ticket stub, postcard, photo, stamp or drawing here

LET NEW ADVENTURES
»» BEGIN →

McArthur-Burney Falls Memorial State Park

County: Shasta

Established: 1920

Acres: 910

Star Rating
☆ ☆ ☆ ☆ ☆

My favorite thing about this place is... _____

Why I went ... _____

Who I went with ... _____

When I went ... _____

What I did... _____

What I saw... _____

What I learned... _____

An unforgettable moment... _____

A laughable moment... _____

A surprising moment... _____

An unforeseeable moment... _____

Wildlife spotted... _____

List
- ☐ _____
- ☐ _____
- ☐ _____
- ☐ _____
- ☐ _____
- ☐ _____
- ☐ _____
- ☐ _____
- ☐ _____
- ☐ _____
- ☐ _____
- ☐ _____
- ☐ _____
- ☐ _____
- ☐ _____
- ☐ _____
- ☐ _____
- ☐ _____
- ☐ _____

Snapped a selfie | Location... _____

Took a park sign photo? - ☐ y ☐ n

The weather was ... ☐ ☐ ☐ ☐ ☐ ☐ ☐

PLAN YOUR TRIP:

RESERVATION INFORMATION:

☐ Day Trip   ☐ Overnight Stay

Reservations required: ☐ y ☐ n

Date reservations made: _____

Refund Policy: ☐ y ☐ n   Site #: _____

Confirmation #: _____

Miles to travel: _____

Time traveling: _____

RV's?: ☐ y ☐ n Largest size RV? _____

Address: _____

_____

Reserved dates: _____

Check-in time: _____ Early check-in?: ☐ y ☐ n

Check-out time: _____ Late check-out?: ☐ y ☐ n

Website: _____

Phone: _____

WiFi: _____ WiFi password: _____

Dog friendly?: ☐ y ☐ n   Open all year?: ☐ y ☐ n

Activities Accomplished:

☐ Archery
☐ Biking
☐ Birding
☐ Boating
☐ Camping
☐ Caving
☐ Geocaching

☐ Fishing
☐ Hiking
☐ Horseback Riding
☐ Hunting
☐ Off-Roading
☐ Paddle Boarding
☐ Photography

☐ Picknicking
☐ Rock Climbing
☐ Shooting Range
☐ Snowshoeing
☐ Stargazing
☐ Swimming
☐ Tennis

☐ Walking
☐ Wildlife Watching
☐ _____
☐ _____
☐ _____
☐ _____
☐ _____

Traveling by:

☐ ☐ ☐ ☐ ☐ ☐ ☐ ☐ ☐ ☐ ☐ ☐

Add your favorite ticket stub, postcard, photo, stamp or drawing here

LET NEW ADVENTURES
»› BEGIN →

Mendocino Headlands State Park

County: Mendocino

Established: 1972   *Acres:* 7,709

Star Rating
☆ ☆ ☆ ☆ ☆

My favorite thing about this place is... _____

Why I went ... _____

Who I went with ... _____

When I went ... _____

What I did... _____

What I saw... _____

What I learned... _____

An unforgettable moment... _____

A laughable moment... _____

A surprising moment... _____

An unforeseeable moment... _____

Wildlife spotted... _____

Snapped a selfie | Location... _____

Took a park sign photo? - ☐ y ☐ n

List
- ☐ _____
- ☐ _____
- ☐ _____
- ☐ _____
- ☐ _____
- ☐ _____
- ☐ _____
- ☐ _____
- ☐ _____
- ☐ _____
- ☐ _____
- ☐ _____
- ☐ _____
- ☐ _____
- ☐ _____
- ☐ _____
- ☐ _____
- ☐ _____
- ☐ _____
- ☐ _____

The weather was ... ☐ ☐ ☐ ☐ ☐ ☐ ☐

PLAN YOUR TRIP:

RESERVATION INFORMATION:

☐ Day Trip   ☐ Overnight Stay

Reservations required: ☐ y ☐ n

Date reservations made: _____

Refund Policy: ☐ y ☐ n   Site #: _____

Confirmation #: _____

Miles to travel: _____

Time traveling: _____

RV's?: ☐ y ☐ n Largest size RV? _____

Address: _____
_____

Reserved dates: _____

Check-in time: _____   Early check-in?: ☐ y ☐ n

Check-out time: _____   Late check-out?: ☐ y ☐ n

Website: _____

Phone: _____

WiFi: _____   WiFi password: _____

Dog friendly?: ☐ y ☐ n   Open all year?: ☐ y ☐ n

Activities Accomplished:

☐ Archery
☐ Biking
☐ Birding
☐ Boating
☐ Camping
☐ Caving
☐ Geocaching

☐ Fishing
☐ Hiking
☐ Horseback Riding
☐ Hunting
☐ Off-Roading
☐ Paddle Boarding
☐ Photography

☐ Picknicking
☐ Rock Climbing
☐ Shooting Range
☐ Snowshoeing
☐ Stargazing
☐ Swimming
☐ Tennis

☐ Walking
☐ Wildlife Watching
☐ _____
☐ _____
☐ _____
☐ _____
☐ _____

Traveling by:

☐ ☐ ☐ ☐ ☐ ☐ ☐ ☐ ☐ ☐ ☐ ☐

Add your favorite ticket stub, postcard, photo, stamp or drawing here

LET NEW ADVENTURES
≫ BEGIN →

Mendocino Woodlands State Park

County: Mendocino

Established: 1977   *Acres: 720*

Star Rating
☆ ☆ ☆ ☆ ☆

My favorite thing about this place is...

Why I went ...

Who I went with ...

When I went ...

What I did...

What I saw...

What I learned...

An unforgettable moment...

A laughable moment...

A surprising moment...

An unforeseeable moment...

Wildlife spotted...

List

- [ ]
- [ ]
- [ ]
- [ ]
- [ ]
- [ ]
- [ ]
- [ ]
- [ ]
- [ ]
- [ ]
- [ ]
- [ ]
- [ ]
- [ ]
- [ ]
- [ ]

Snapped a selfie | Location...

Took a park sign photo? - ☐ y ☐ n

The weather was ...
☐ ☐ ☐ ☐ ☐ ☐ ☐

PLAN YOUR TRIP:

☐ Day Trip   ☐ Overnight Stay

Reservations required: ☐ y ☐ n

Date reservations made: _____

Refund Policy: ☐ y ☐ n Site #: _____

Confirmation #: _____

Miles to travel: _____

Time traveling: _____

RV's?: ☐ y ☐ n Largest size RV? _____

Activities Accomplished:

☐ Archery   ☐ Fishing
☐ Biking   ☐ Hiking
☐ Birding   ☐ Horseback Riding
☐ Boating   ☐ Hunting
☐ Camping   ☐ Off-Roading
☐ Caving   ☐ Paddle Boarding
☐ Geocaching   ☐ Photography

☐ Picknicking   ☐ Walking
☐ Rock Climbing   ☐ Wildlife Watching
☐ Shooting Range   ☐ _____
☐ Snowshoeing   ☐ _____
☐ Stargazing   ☐ _____
☐ Swimming   ☐ _____
☐ Tennis   ☐ _____

RESERVATION INFORMATION:

Address: _____
_____

Reserved dates: _____

Check-in time: _____   Early check-in?: ☐ y ☐ n

Check-out time: _____   Late check-out?: ☐ y ☐ n

Website: _____

Phone: _____

WiFi: _____   WiFi password: _____

Dog friendly?: ☐ y ☐ n   Open all year?: ☐ y ☐ n

Traveling by:

☐ ☐ ☐ ☐ ☐ ☐ ☐ ☐ ☐ ☐ ☐ ☐

Add your favorite ticket stub, postcard, photo, stamp or drawing here

LET NEW ADVENTURES
》 BEGIN →

Montańa de Oro State Park

County: San Luis Obispo

Established: 1934

Acres: 10,366

Star Rating
☆ ☆ ☆ ☆ ☆

My favorite thing about this place is... _____

Why I went ... _____

Who I went with ... _____

When I went ... _____

What I did... _____

What I saw... _____

What I learned... _____

An unforgettable moment... _____

A laughable moment... _____

A surprising moment... _____

An unforeseeable moment... _____

Wildlife spotted... _____

List
- [ ] _____
- [ ] _____
- [ ] _____
- [ ] _____
- [ ] _____
- [ ] _____
- [ ] _____
- [ ] _____
- [ ] _____
- [ ] _____
- [ ] _____
- [ ] _____
- [ ] _____
- [ ] _____
- [ ] _____
- [ ] _____
- [ ] _____
- [ ] _____
- [ ] _____
- [ ] _____

Snapped a selfie | Location... _____

Took a park sign photo? - ☐ y ☐ n

The weather was ...
☐ ☐ ☐ ☐ ☐ ☐ ☐

PLAN YOUR TRIP:

☐ Day Trip   ☐ Overnight Stay

Reservations required: ☐ y ☐ n

Date reservations made: _____

Refund Policy: ☐ y ☐ n Site #: _____

Confirmation #: _____

Miles to travel: _____

Time traveling: _____

RV's?: ☐ y ☐ n Largest size RV? _____

Activities Accomplished:

☐ Archery   ☐ Fishing   ☐ Picknicking   ☐ Walking
☐ Biking   ☐ Hiking   ☐ Rock Climbing   ☐ Wildlife Watching
☐ Birding   ☐ Horseback Riding ☐ Shooting Range   ☐ _____
☐ Boating   ☐ Hunting   ☐ Snowshoeing   ☐ _____
☐ Camping   ☐ Off-Roading   ☐ Stargazing   ☐ _____
☐ Caving   ☐ Paddle Boarding ☐ Swimming   ☐ _____
☐ Geocaching   ☐ Photography   ☐ Tennis   ☐ _____

RESERVATION INFORMATION:

Address: _____
_____

Reserved dates: _____

Check-in time: _____   Early check-in?: ☐ y ☐ n

Check-out time: _____ Late check-out?: ☐ y ☐ n

Website: _____

Phone: _____

WiFi: _____ WiFi password: _____

Dog friendly?: ☐ y ☐ n   Open all year?: ☐ y ☐ n

Traveling by:

☐ ☐ ☐ ☐ ☐ ☐ ☐ ☐ ☐ ☐ ☐ ☐

Add your favorite ticket stub, postcard, photo, stamp or drawing here

LET NEW ADVENTURES
≫ BEGIN →

Morro Bay State Park

County: San Luis Obispo

Established: 1934

Acres: 2,783

Star Rating

☆ ☆ ☆ ☆ ☆

My favorite thing about this place is... _____

Why I went ... _____

Who I went with ... _____

When I went ... _____

What I did... _____

What I saw... _____

What I learned... _____

An unforgettable moment... _____

A laughable moment... _____

A surprising moment... _____

An unforeseeable moment... _____

Wildlife spotted... _____

Snapped a selfie | Location... _____

Took a park sign photo? - ☐ y ☐ n

List
- ☐ _____
- ☐ _____
- ☐ _____
- ☐ _____
- ☐ _____
- ☐ _____
- ☐ _____
- ☐ _____
- ☐ _____
- ☐ _____
- ☐ _____
- ☐ _____
- ☐ _____
- ☐ _____
- ☐ _____
- ☐ _____
- ☐ _____
- ☐ _____

The weather was ...
☐ ☐ ☐ ☐ ☐ ☐ ☐

PLAN YOUR TRIP:

☐ Day Trip   ☐ Overnight Stay

Reservations required: ☐ y ☐ n

Date reservations made: _____

Refund Policy: ☐ y ☐ n Site #: _____

Confirmation #: _____

Miles to travel: _____

Time traveling: _____

RV's?: ☐ y ☐ n Largest size RV? _____

Activities Accomplished:

☐ Archery
☐ Biking
☐ Birding
☐ Boating
☐ Camping
☐ Caving
☐ Geocaching

☐ Fishing
☐ Hiking
☐ Horseback Riding
☐ Hunting
☐ Off-Roading
☐ Paddle Boarding
☐ Photography

☐ Picknicking
☐ Rock Climbing
☐ Shooting Range
☐ Snowshoeing
☐ Stargazing
☐ Swimming
☐ Tennis

☐ Walking
☐ Wildlife Watching
☐ _____
☐ _____
☐ _____
☐ _____
☐ _____

Traveling by:

☐ ☐ ☐ ☐ ☐ ☐ ☐ ☐ ☐ ☐ ☐ ☐

RESERVATION INFORMATION:

Address: _____
_____

Reserved dates: _____

Check-in time: _____   Early check-in?: ☐ y ☐ n

Check-out time: _____   Late check-out?: ☐ y ☐ n

Website: _____

Phone: _____

WiFi: _____ WiFi password: _____

Dog friendly?: ☐ y ☐ n   Open all year?: ☐ y ☐ n

Add your favorite ticket stub, postcard, photo, stamp or drawing here

LET NEW ADVENTURES
≫ BEGIN →

Mount Diablo State Park

County: Contra Costa

Established: 1931

Acres: 20,124

Star Rating
☆ ☆ ☆ ☆ ☆

My favorite thing about this place is...

Why I went ...

Who I went with ...

When I went ...

What I did...

What I saw...

What I learned...

An unforgettable moment...

A laughable moment...

A surprising moment...

An unforeseeable moment...

Wildlife spotted...

List
- [ ]
- [ ]
- [ ]
- [ ]
- [ ]
- [ ]
- [ ]
- [ ]
- [ ]
- [ ]
- [ ]
- [ ]
- [ ]
- [ ]
- [ ]
- [ ]
- [ ]
- [ ]
- [ ]
- [ ]
- [ ]

Snapped a selfie | Location...

Took a park sign photo? - ☐ y ☐ n

The weather was ... ☐ ☐ ☐ ☐ ☐ ☐ ☐

PLAN YOUR TRIP:

☐ Day Trip   ☐ Overnight Stay

Reservations required: ☐ y ☐ n

Date reservations made: _____

Refund Policy: ☐ y ☐ n Site #: _____

Confirmation #: _____

Miles to travel: _____

Time traveling: _____

RV's?: ☐ y ☐ n Largest size RV? _____

Activities Accomplished:

☐ Archery   ☐ Fishing   ☐ Picknicking   ☐ Walking
☐ Biking   ☐ Hiking   ☐ Rock Climbing   ☐ Wildlife Watching
☐ Birding   ☐ Horseback Riding ☐ Shooting Range   ☐ _____
☐ Boating   ☐ Hunting   ☐ Snowshoeing   ☐ _____
☐ Camping   ☐ Off-Roading   ☐ Stargazing   ☐ _____
☐ Caving   ☐ Paddle Boarding   ☐ Swimming   ☐ _____
☐ Geocaching   ☐ Photography   ☐ Tennis   ☐ _____

Traveling by:

☐ ☐ ☐ ☐ ☐ ☐ ☐ ☐ ☐ ☐ ☐ ☐

RESERVATION INFORMATION:

Address: _____
_____

Reserved dates: _____

Check-in time: _____   Early check-in?: ☐ y ☐ n

Check-out time: _____   Late check-out?: ☐ y ☐ n

Website: _____

Phone: _____

WiFi: _____   WiFi password: _____

Dog friendly?: ☐ y ☐ n   Open all year?: ☐ y ☐ n

Add your favorite ticket stub, postcard, photo, stamp or drawing here

LET NEW ADVENTURES
≫ BEGIN →

MOUNT SAN JACINTO STATE PARK

County: Riverside

Established: 1930   *Acres:* 13,718

_____
Star Rating
☆ ☆ ☆ ☆ ☆

My favorite thing about this place is... _____

Why I went ... _____

Who I went with ... _____

When I went ... _____

What I did... _____

What I saw... _____

What I learned... _____

An unforgettable moment... _____

A laughable moment... _____

A surprising moment... _____

An unforeseeable moment... _____

Wildlife spotted... _____

Snapped a selfie | Location... _____

Took a park sign photo? - ☐ y ☐ n

List
- ☐ _____
- ☐ _____
- ☐ _____
- ☐ _____
- ☐ _____
- ☐ _____
- ☐ _____
- ☐ _____
- ☐ _____
- ☐ _____
- ☐ _____
- ☐ _____
- ☐ _____
- ☐ _____
- ☐ _____
- ☐ _____
- ☐ _____
- ☐ _____

The weather was ...
☐ ☐ ☐ ☐ ☐ ☐ ☐

PLAN YOUR TRIP:

☐ Day Trip   ☐ Overnight Stay

Reservations required: ☐ y ☐ n

Date reservations made: _____

Refund Policy: ☐ y ☐ n Site #: _____

Confirmation #: _____

Miles to travel: _____

Time traveling: _____

RV's?: ☐ y ☐ n Largest size RV? _____

Activities Accomplished:

☐ Archery   ☐ Fishing
☐ Biking   ☐ Hiking
☐ Birding   ☐ Horseback Riding
☐ Boating   ☐ Hunting
☐ Camping   ☐ Off-Roading
☐ Caving   ☐ Paddle Boarding
☐ Geocaching   ☐ Photography

☐ Picknicking   ☐ Walking
☐ Rock Climbing   ☐ Wildlife Watching
☐ Shooting Range   ☐ _____
☐ Snowshoeing   ☐ _____
☐ Stargazing   ☐ _____
☐ Swimming   ☐ _____
☐ Tennis   ☐ _____

RESERVATION INFORMATION:

Address: _____
_____

Reserved dates: _____

Check-in time: _____ Early check-in?: ☐ y ☐ n

Check-out time: _____ Late check-out?: ☐ y ☐ n

Website: _____

Phone: _____

WiFi: _____ WiFi password: _____

Dog friendly?: ☐ y ☐ n   Open all year?: ☐ y ☐ n

Traveling by:

☐ ☐ ☐ ☐ ☐ ☐ ☐ ☐ ☐ ☐ ☐ ☐

Add your favorite ticket stub, postcard, photo, stamp or drawing here

LET NEW ADVENTURES
»» BEGIN →

Mount Tamalpais State Park

County: Marin

Established: 1928   *Acres:* 6,243

Star Rating

☆ ☆ ☆ ☆ ☆

My favorite thing about this place is... _____

Why I went ... _____

Who I went with ... _____

When I went ... _____

What I did... _____

What I saw... _____

What I learned... _____

An unforgettable moment... _____

A laughable moment... _____

A surprising moment... _____

An unforeseeable moment... _____

Wildlife spotted... _____

📷 Snapped a selfie | Location... _____

📷 Took a park sign photo? - ☐ y ☐ n

List

☐ _____
☐ _____
☐ _____
☐ _____
☐ _____
☐ _____
☐ _____
☐ _____
☐ _____
☐ _____
☐ _____
☐ _____
☐ _____
☐ _____
☐ _____
☐ _____
☐ _____
☐ _____

The weather was ...   ☐ ☐ ☐ ☐ ☐ ☐ ☐

PLAN YOUR TRIP:

☐ Day Trip   ☐ Overnight Stay

Reservations required: ☐ y ☐ n

Date reservations made: _____

Refund Policy: ☐ y ☐ n Site #: _____

Confirmation #: _____

Miles to travel: _____

Time traveling: _____

RV's?: ☐ y ☐ n Largest size RV? _____

Activities Accomplished:

☐ Archery
☐ Biking
☐ Birding
☐ Boating
☐ Camping
☐ Caving
☐ Geocaching

☐ Fishing
☐ Hiking
☐ Horseback Riding
☐ Hunting
☐ Off-Roading
☐ Paddle Boarding
☐ Photography

☐ Picknicking
☐ Rock Climbing
☐ Shooting Range
☐ Snowshoeing
☐ Stargazing
☐ Swimming
☐ Tennis

☐ Walking
☐ Wildlife Watching
☐ _____
☐ _____
☐ _____
☐ _____
☐ _____

RESERVATION INFORMATION:

Address: _____
_____

Reserved dates: _____

Check-in time: _____ Early check-in?: ☐ y ☐ n

Check-out time: _____ Late check-out?: ☐ y ☐ n

Website: _____

Phone: _____

WiFi: _____ WiFi password: _____

Dog friendly?: ☐ y ☐ n   Open all year?: ☐ y ☐ n

Traveling by:

☐ ☐ ☐ ☐ ☐ ☐ ☐ ☐ ☐ ☐ ☐ ☐

Add your favorite ticket stub, postcard, photo, stamp or drawing here

LET NEW ADVENTURES
»» BEGIN →

Navarro River Redwoods State Park

County: Mendocino

Established: 1928   *Acres:* 727

_____
Star Rating
☆ ☆ ☆ ☆ ☆

My favorite thing about this place is... _____

Why I went ... _____

Who I went with ... _____

When I went ... _____

What I did... _____

What I saw... _____

What I learned... _____

An unforgettable moment... _____

A laughable moment... _____

A surprising moment... _____

An unforeseeable moment... _____

Wildlife spotted... _____

📷 Snapped a selfie | Location... _____

📷 Took a park sign photo? - ☐ y ☐ n

List
- ☐ _____
- ☐ _____
- ☐ _____
- ☐ _____
- ☐ _____
- ☐ _____
- ☐ _____
- ☐ _____
- ☐ _____
- ☐ _____
- ☐ _____
- ☐ _____
- ☐ _____
- ☐ _____
- ☐ _____
- ☐ _____
- ☐ _____
- ☐ _____
- ☐ _____

The weather was ... ☐ ☐ ☐ ☐ ☐ ☐ ☐

PLAN YOUR TRIP:

☐ Day Trip   ☐ Overnight Stay

Reservations required: ☐ y ☐ n

Date reservations made: _____

Refund Policy: ☐ y ☐ n Site #: _____

Confirmation #: _____

Miles to travel: _____

Time traveling: _____

RV's?: ☐ y ☐ n Largest size RV? _____

Activities Accomplished:

☐ Archery
☐ Biking
☐ Birding
☐ Boating
☐ Camping
☐ Caving
☐ Geocaching

☐ Fishing
☐ Hiking
☐ Horseback Riding
☐ Hunting
☐ Off-Roading
☐ Paddle Boarding
☐ Photography

☐ Picknicking
☐ Rock Climbing
☐ Shooting Range
☐ Snowshoeing
☐ Stargazing
☐ Swimming
☐ Tennis

☐ Walking
☐ Wildlife Watching
☐ _____
☐ _____
☐ _____
☐ _____
☐ _____

Traveling by:

☐ ☐ ☐ ☐ ☐ ☐ ☐ ☐ ☐ ☐ ☐ ☐

RESERVATION INFORMATION:

Address: _____
_____

Reserved dates: _____

Check-in time: _____   Early check-in?: ☐ y ☐ n

Check-out time: _____   Late check-out?: ☐ y ☐ n

Website: _____

Phone: _____

WiFi: _____   WiFi password: _____

Dog friendly?: ☐ y ☐ n   Open all year?: ☐ y ☐ n

Add your favorite ticket stub, postcard, photo, stamp or drawing here

LET NEW ADVENTURES
≫ BEGIN →

Pacheco State Park

County: Merced and Santa Clara

Established: 1995

Acres: 6,894

Star Rating
☆☆☆☆☆

My favorite thing about this place is...

Why I went ...

Who I went with ...

When I went ...

What I did...

What I saw...

What I learned...

An unforgettable moment...

A laughable moment...

A surprising moment...

An unforeseeable moment...

Wildlife spotted...

Snapped a selfie | Location...

Took a park sign photo? - ☐ y ☐ n

List

☐ _____
☐ _____
☐ _____
☐ _____
☐ _____
☐ _____
☐ _____
☐ _____
☐ _____
☐ _____
☐ _____
☐ _____
☐ _____
☐ _____
☐ _____
☐ _____
☐ _____
☐ _____
☐ _____

The weather was ...

☐ ☐ ☐ ☐ ☐ ☐ ☐

PLAN YOUR TRIP:

☐ Day Trip   ☐ Overnight Stay

Reservations required: ☐ y ☐ n

Date reservations made: _____

Refund Policy: ☐ y ☐ n Site #: _____

Confirmation #: _____

Miles to travel: _____

Time traveling: _____

RV's?: ☐ y ☐ n Largest size RV? _____

Activities Accomplished:

☐ Archery   ☐ Fishing   ☐ Picknicking   ☐ Walking
☐ Biking   ☐ Hiking   ☐ Rock Climbing   ☐ Wildlife Watching
☐ Birding   ☐ Horseback Riding ☐ Shooting Range   ☐ _____
☐ Boating   ☐ Hunting   ☐ Snowshoeing   ☐ _____
☐ Camping   ☐ Off-Roading   ☐ Stargazing   ☐ _____
☐ Caving   ☐ Paddle Boarding ☐ Swimming   ☐ _____
☐ Geocaching   ☐ Photography   ☐ Tennis   ☐ _____

Traveling by:

☐ ☐ ☐ ☐ ☐ ☐ ☐ ☐ ☐ ☐ ☐ ☐

RESERVATION INFORMATION:

Address: _____
_____

Reserved dates: _____

Check-in time: _____ Early check-in?: ☐ y ☐ n

Check-out time: _____ Late check-out?: ☐ y ☐ n

Website: _____

Phone: _____

WiFi: _____ WiFi password: _____

Dog friendly?: ☐ y ☐ n   Open all year?: ☐ y ☐ n

Add your favorite ticket stub, postcard, photo, stamp or drawing here

LET NEW ADVENTURES
»» BEGIN →

Palomar Mountain State Park

County: San Diego

Established: 1932

Acres: 1,909

Star Rating
☆ ☆ ☆ ☆ ☆

My favorite thing about this place is... _____

Why I went ... _____

Who I went with ... _____

When I went ... _____

What I did... _____

What I saw... _____

What I learned... _____

An unforgettable moment... _____

A laughable moment... _____

A surprising moment... _____

An unforeseeable moment... _____

Wildlife spotted... _____

Snapped a selfie | Location... _____

Took a park sign photo? - ☐ y ☐ n

List
- ☐ _____
- ☐ _____
- ☐ _____
- ☐ _____
- ☐ _____
- ☐ _____
- ☐ _____
- ☐ _____
- ☐ _____
- ☐ _____
- ☐ _____
- ☐ _____
- ☐ _____
- ☐ _____
- ☐ _____
- ☐ _____
- ☐ _____
- ☐ _____

The weather was ...
☐ ☐ ☐ ☐ ☐ ☐ ☐

PLAN YOUR TRIP:

☐ Day Trip   ☐ Overnight Stay

Reservations required: ☐y ☐n

Date reservations made: _____

Refund Policy: ☐y ☐n Site #: _____

Confirmation #: _____

Miles to travel: _____

Time traveling: _____

RV's?: ☐y ☐n Largest size RV? _____

Activities Accomplished:

☐ Archery
☐ Biking
☐ Birding
☐ Boating
☐ Camping
☐ Caving
☐ Geocaching

☐ Fishing
☐ Hiking
☐ Horseback Riding
☐ Hunting
☐ Off-Roading
☐ Paddle Boarding
☐ Photography

☐ Picknicking
☐ Rock Climbing
☐ Shooting Range
☐ Snowshoeing
☐ Stargazing
☐ Swimming
☐ Tennis

☐ Walking
☐ Wildlife Watching
☐ _____
☐ _____
☐ _____
☐ _____
☐ _____

RESERVATION INFORMATION:

Address: _____
_____

Reserved dates: _____

Check-in time: _____   Early check-in?: ☐y ☐n

Check-out time: _____   Late check-out?: ☐y ☐n

Website: _____

Phone: _____

WiFi: _____   WiFi password: _____

Dog friendly?: ☐y ☐n   Open all year?: ☐y ☐n

Traveling by:

☐ ☐ ☐ ☐ ☐ ☐ ☐ ☐ ☐ ☐ ☐ ☐

Add your favorite ticket stub, postcard, photo, stamp or drawing here

LET NEW ADVENTURES
»» BEGIN →

PATRICK'S POINT STATE PARK

County: Humboldt

Established: 1930

Acres: 652

Star Rating
☆ ☆ ☆ ☆ ☆

My favorite thing about this place is... _____

Why I went ... _____

Who I went with ... _____

When I went ... _____

What I did... _____

What I saw... _____

What I learned... _____

An unforgettable moment... _____

A laughable moment... _____

A surprising moment... _____

An unforeseeable moment... _____

Wildlife spotted... _____

List
- ☐ _____
- ☐ _____
- ☐ _____
- ☐ _____
- ☐ _____
- ☐ _____
- ☐ _____
- ☐ _____
- ☐ _____
- ☐ _____
- ☐ _____
- ☐ _____
- ☐ _____
- ☐ _____
- ☐ _____
- ☐ _____
- ☐ _____
- ☐ _____

Snapped a selfie | Location... _____

Took a park sign photo? - ☐ y ☐ n

The weather was ...
☐ ☐ ☐ ☐ ☐ ☐ ☐

PLAN YOUR TRIP:

RESERVATION INFORMATION:

☐ Day Trip   ☐ Overnight Stay

Reservations required: ☐ y ☐ n

Date reservations made: _____

Refund Policy: ☐ y ☐ n Site #: _____

Confirmation #: _____

Miles to travel: _____

Time traveling: _____

RV's?: ☐ y ☐ n Largest size RV? _____

Address: _____
_____

Reserved dates: _____

Check-in time: _____ Early check-in?: ☐ y ☐ n

Check-out time: _____ Late check-out?: ☐ y ☐ n

Website: _____

Phone: _____

WiFi: _____ WiFi password: _____

Dog friendly?: ☐ y ☐ n   Open all year?: ☐ y ☐ n

Activities Accomplished:

☐ Archery
☐ Biking
☐ Birding
☐ Boating
☐ Camping
☐ Caving
☐ Geocaching

☐ Fishing
☐ Hiking
☐ Horseback Riding
☐ Hunting
☐ Off-Roading
☐ Paddle Boarding
☐ Photography

☐ Picknicking
☐ Rock Climbing
☐ Shooting Range
☐ Snowshoeing
☐ Stargazing
☐ Swimming
☐ Tennis

☐ Walking
☐ Wildlife Watching
☐ _____
☐ _____
☐ _____
☐ _____
☐ _____

Traveling by:

☐ ☐ ☐ ☐ ☐ ☐ ☐ ☐ ☐ ☐ ☐ ☐

Add your favorite ticket stub, postcard, photo, stamp or drawing here

LET NEW ADVENTURES
>>> BEGIN →

Pfeiffer Big Sur State Park

County: Monterey

Established: 1933

Acres: 1,391

Star Rating

☆ ☆ ☆ ☆ ☆

My favorite thing about this place is... _____

Why I went ... _____

Who I went with ... _____

When I went ... _____

What I did... _____

What I saw... _____

What I learned... _____

An unforgettable moment... _____

A laughable moment... _____

A surprising moment... _____

An unforeseeable moment... _____

Wildlife spotted... _____

List

- [ ] _____
- [ ] _____
- [ ] _____
- [ ] _____
- [ ] _____
- [ ] _____
- [ ] _____
- [ ] _____
- [ ] _____
- [ ] _____
- [ ] _____
- [ ] _____
- [ ] _____
- [ ] _____
- [ ] _____
- [ ] _____
- [ ] _____
- [ ] _____
- [ ] _____
- [ ] _____

Snapped a selfie | Location... _____

Took a park sign photo? - ☐ y ☐ n

The weather was ... ☐ ☐ ☐ ☐ ☐ ☐ ☐

PLAN YOUR TRIP:

RESERVATION INFORMATION:

☐ Day Trip   ☐ Overnight Stay

Reservations required: ☐ y ☐ n

Date reservations made: _____

Refund Policy: ☐ y ☐ n Site #: _____

Confirmation #: _____

Miles to travel: _____

Time traveling: _____

RV's?: ☐ y ☐ n Largest size RV? _____

Address: _____
_____

Reserved dates: _____

Check-in time: _____ Early check-in?: ☐ y ☐ n

Check-out time: _____ Late check-out?: ☐ y ☐ n

Website: _____

Phone: _____

WiFi: _____ WiFi password: _____

Dog friendly?: ☐ y ☐ n   Open all year?: ☐ y ☐ n

Activities Accomplished:

☐ Archery
☐ Biking
☐ Birding
☐ Boating
☐ Camping
☐ Caving
☐ Geocaching

☐ Fishing
☐ Hiking
☐ Horseback Riding
☐ Hunting
☐ Off-Roading
☐ Paddle Boarding
☐ Photography

☐ Picknicking
☐ Rock Climbing
☐ Shooting Range
☐ Snowshoeing
☐ Stargazing
☐ Swimming
☐ Tennis

☐ Walking
☐ Wildlife Watching
☐ _____
☐ _____
☐ _____
☐ _____
☐ _____

Traveling by:

☐   ☐   ☐   ☐   ☐   ☐   ☐   ☐   ☐   ☐   ☐   ☐

Add your favorite ticket stub, postcard, photo, stamp or drawing here

LET NEW ADVENTURES
≫ BEGIN →

Placerita Canyon State Park

County: Los Angeles

Established: 1949   *Acres:* 342

Star Rating

☆ ☆ ☆ ☆ ☆

My favorite thing about this place is... _____

Why I went ... _____

Who I went with ... _____

When I went ... _____

What I did... _____

What I saw... _____

What I learned... _____

An unforgettable moment... _____

A laughable moment... _____

A surprising moment... _____

An unforeseeable moment... _____

Wildlife spotted... _____

Snapped a selfie | Location... _____

Took a park sign photo? - ☐ y ☐ n

List

☐ _____
☐ _____
☐ _____
☐ _____
☐ _____
☐ _____
☐ _____
☐ _____
☐ _____
☐ _____
☐ _____
☐ _____
☐ _____
☐ _____
☐ _____
☐ _____
☐ _____
☐ _____

The weather was ... ☐ ☐ ☐ ☐ ☐ ☐ ☐

PLAN YOUR TRIP:

☐ Day Trip   ☐ Overnight Stay

Reservations required: ☐ y ☐ n

Date reservations made: _____

Refund Policy: ☐ y ☐ n Site #: _____

Confirmation #: _____

Miles to travel: _____

Time traveling: _____

RV's?: ☐ y ☐ n Largest size RV? _____

Activities Accomplished:

☐ Archery
☐ Biking
☐ Birding
☐ Boating
☐ Camping
☐ Caving
☐ Geocaching

☐ Fishing
☐ Hiking
☐ Horseback Riding
☐ Hunting
☐ Off-Roading
☐ Paddle Boarding
☐ Photography

☐ Picknicking
☐ Rock Climbing
☐ Shooting Range
☐ Snowshoeing
☐ Stargazing
☐ Swimming
☐ Tennis

☐ Walking
☐ Wildlife Watching
☐ _____
☐ _____
☐ _____
☐ _____
☐ _____

RESERVATION INFORMATION:

Address: _____
_____

Reserved dates: _____

Check-in time: _____ Early check-in?: ☐ y ☐ n

Check-out time: _____ Late check-out?: ☐ y ☐ n

Website: _____

Phone: _____

WiFi: _____ WiFi password: _____

Dog friendly?: ☐ y ☐ n   Open all year?: ☐ y ☐ n

Traveling by:

☐ ☐ ☐ ☐ ☐ ☐ ☐ ☐ ☐ ☐ ☐ ☐

Add your favorite ticket stub, postcard, photo, stamp or drawing here

LET NEW ADVENTURES
»» BEGIN →

Plumas-Eureka State Park

County: Plumas

Established: 1959

Acres: 4,424

Star Rating
☆ ☆ ☆ ☆ ☆

My favorite thing about this place is...

Why I went ...

Who I went with ...

When I went ...

What I did...

What I saw...

What I learned...

An unforgettable moment...

A laughable moment...

A surprising moment...

An unforeseeable moment...

Wildlife spotted...

Snapped a selfie | Location...

Took a park sign photo? - ☐ y ☐ n

List

☐
☐
☐
☐
☐
☐
☐
☐
☐
☐
☐
☐
☐
☐
☐
☐
☐
☐
☐

The weather was ...
☐ ☐ ☐ ☐ ☐ ☐ ☐

PLAN YOUR TRIP:

☐ Day Trip   ☐ Overnight Stay

Reservations required: ☐ y ☐ n

Date reservations made: _____

Refund Policy: ☐ y ☐ n   Site #: _____

Confirmation #: _____

Miles to travel: _____

Time traveling: _____

RV's?: ☐ y ☐ n Largest size RV? _____

Activities Accomplished:

☐ Archery
☐ Biking
☐ Birding
☐ Boating
☐ Camping
☐ Caving
☐ Geocaching

☐ Fishing
☐ Hiking
☐ Horseback Riding
☐ Hunting
☐ Off-Roading
☐ Paddle Boarding
☐ Photography

☐ Picknicking
☐ Rock Climbing
☐ Shooting Range
☐ Snowshoeing
☐ Stargazing
☐ Swimming
☐ Tennis

☐ Walking
☐ Wildlife Watching
☐ _____
☐ _____
☐ _____
☐ _____
☐ _____

RESERVATION INFORMATION:

Address: _____
_____

Reserved dates: _____

Check-in time: _____   Early check-in?: ☐ y ☐ n

Check-out time: _____   Late check-out?: ☐ y ☐ n

Website: _____

Phone: _____

WiFi: _____   WiFi password: _____

Dog friendly?: ☐ y ☐ n   Open all year?: ☐ y ☐ n

Traveling by:

☐ ☐ ☐ ☐ ☐ ☐ ☐ ☐ ☐ ☐ ☐ ☐

Add your favorite ticket stub, postcard, photo, stamp or drawing here

LET NEW ADVENTURES
>>> BEGIN →

Point Mugu State Park

County: Los Angeles

Established: 1966

Acres: 13,947

Star Rating

☆ ☆ ☆ ☆ ☆

My favorite thing about this place is...

Why I went ...

Who I went with ...

When I went ...

What I did...

What I saw...

What I learned...

An unforgettable moment...

A laughable moment...

A surprising moment...

An unforeseeable moment...

Wildlife spotted...

List

- [ ]
- [ ]
- [ ]
- [ ]
- [ ]
- [ ]
- [ ]
- [ ]
- [ ]
- [ ]
- [ ]
- [ ]
- [ ]
- [ ]
- [ ]
- [ ]
- [ ]
- [ ]
- [ ]
- [ ]

Snapped a selfie | Location...

Took a park sign photo? - ☐ y ☐ n

The weather was ... ☐ ☐ ☐ ☐ ☐ ☐ ☐

PLAN YOUR TRIP:

RESERVATION INFORMATION:

☐ Day Trip   ☐ Overnight Stay

Reservations required: ☐ y ☐ n

Date reservations made: _____

Refund Policy: ☐ y ☐ n Site #: _____

Confirmation #: _____

Miles to travel: _____

Time traveling: _____

RV's?: ☐ y ☐ n Largest size RV? _____

Address: _____
_____

Reserved dates: _____

Check-in time: _____ Early check-in?: ☐ y ☐ n

Check-out time: _____ Late check-out?: ☐ y ☐ n

Website: _____

Phone: _____

WiFi: _____ WiFi password: _____

Dog friendly?: ☐ y ☐ n   Open all year?: ☐ y ☐ n

Activities Accomplished:

☐ Archery
☐ Biking
☐ Birding
☐ Boating
☐ Camping
☐ Caving
☐ Geocaching

☐ Fishing
☐ Hiking
☐ Horseback Riding
☐ Hunting
☐ Off-Roading
☐ Paddle Boarding
☐ Photography

☐ Picknicking
☐ Rock Climbing
☐ Shooting Range
☐ Snowshoeing
☐ Stargazing
☐ Swimming
☐ Tennis

☐ Walking
☐ Wildlife Watching
☐ _____
☐ _____
☐ _____
☐ _____
☐ _____

Traveling by:

☐ ☐ ☐ ☐ ☐ ☐ ☐ ☐ ☐ ☐ ☐ ☐

Add your favorite ticket stub, postcard, photo, stamp or drawing here

LET NEW ADVENTURES
>>> BEGIN →

Portola Redwoods State Park

County: San Mateo

Established: 1945

Acres: 2,608

Star Rating
☆ ☆ ☆ ☆ ☆

My favorite thing about this place is... _____

Why I went ... _____

Who I went with ... _____

When I went ... _____

What I did... _____

What I saw... _____

What I learned... _____

An unforgettable moment... _____

A laughable moment... _____

A surprising moment... _____

An unforeseeable moment... _____

Wildlife spotted... _____

List

- ☐ _____
- ☐ _____
- ☐ _____
- ☐ _____
- ☐ _____
- ☐ _____
- ☐ _____
- ☐ _____
- ☐ _____
- ☐ _____
- ☐ _____
- ☐ _____
- ☐ _____
- ☐ _____
- ☐ _____
- ☐ _____
- ☐ _____
- ☐ _____

Snapped a selfie | Location... _____

Took a park sign photo? - ☐ y ☐ n

The weather was ...
☐ ☐ ☐ ☐ ☐ ☐ ☐

PLAN YOUR TRIP:

RESERVATION INFORMATION:

☐ Day Trip   ☐ Overnight Stay

Reservations required: ☐ y ☐ n

Date reservations made: _____

Refund Policy: ☐ y ☐ n   Site #: _____

Confirmation #: _____

Miles to travel: _____

Time traveling: _____

RV's?: ☐ y ☐ n Largest size RV? _____

Activities Accomplished:

Address: _____
_____

Reserved dates: _____

Check-in time: _____   Early check-in?: ☐ y ☐ n

Check-out time: _____ Late check-out?: ☐ y ☐ n

Website: _____

Phone: _____

WiFi: _____   WiFi password: _____

Dog friendly?: ☐ y ☐ n   Open all year?: ☐ y ☐ n

☐ Archery
☐ Biking
☐ Birding
☐ Boating
☐ Camping
☐ Caving
☐ Geocaching

☐ Fishing
☐ Hiking
☐ Horseback Riding
☐ Hunting
☐ Off-Roading
☐ Paddle Boarding
☐ Photography

☐ Picknicking
☐ Rock Climbing
☐ Shooting Range
☐ Snowshoeing
☐ Stargazing
☐ Swimming
☐ Tennis

☐ Walking
☐ Wildlife Watching
☐ _____
☐ _____
☐ _____
☐ _____
☐ _____

Traveling by:

☐ ☐ ☐ ☐ ☐ ☐ ☐ ☐ ☐ ☐ ☐ ☐

Add your favorite ticket stub, postcard, photo, stamp or drawing here

LET NEW ADVENTURES
»» BEGIN →

Prairie Creek Redwoods State Park

County: Humboldt

Established: 1923

Acres: 14,187

_____
Star Rating
☆ ☆ ☆ ☆ ☆

My favorite thing about this place is... _____

Why I went ... _____

Who I went with ... _____

When I went ... _____

What I did... _____

What I saw... _____

What I learned... _____

An unforgettable moment... _____

A laughable moment... _____

A surprising moment... _____

An unforeseeable moment... _____

Wildlife spotted... _____

List
- [ ] _____
- [ ] _____
- [ ] _____
- [ ] _____
- [ ] _____
- [ ] _____
- [ ] _____
- [ ] _____
- [ ] _____
- [ ] _____
- [ ] _____
- [ ] _____
- [ ] _____
- [ ] _____
- [ ] _____
- [ ] _____
- [ ] _____
- [ ] _____
- [ ] _____
- [ ] _____

📷 Snapped a selfie | Location... _____

📷 Took a park sign photo? - ☐ y ☐ n

The weather was ...
☐ ☐ ☐ ☐ ☐ ☐ ☐

PLAN YOUR TRIP:

☐ Day Trip   ☐ Overnight Stay

Reservations required: ☐ y ☐ n

Date reservations made: _____

Refund Policy: ☐ y ☐ n   Site #: _____

Confirmation #: _____

Miles to travel: _____

Time traveling: _____

RV's?: ☐ y ☐ n Largest size RV? _____

Activities Accomplished:

☐ Archery
☐ Biking
☐ Birding
☐ Boating
☐ Camping
☐ Caving
☐ Geocaching

☐ Fishing
☐ Hiking
☐ Horseback Riding
☐ Hunting
☐ Off-Roading
☐ Paddle Boarding
☐ Photography

☐ Picknicking
☐ Rock Climbing
☐ Shooting Range
☐ Snowshoeing
☐ Stargazing
☐ Swimming
☐ Tennis

☐ Walking
☐ Wildlife Watching
☐ _____
☐ _____
☐ _____
☐ _____
☐ _____

RESERVATION INFORMATION:

Address: _____
_____

Reserved dates: _____

Check-in time: _____   Early check-in?: ☐ y ☐ n

Check-out time: _____   Late check-out?: ☐ y ☐ n

Website: _____

Phone: _____

WiFi: _____   WiFi password: _____

Dog friendly?: ☐ y ☐ n   Open all year?: ☐ y ☐ n

Traveling by:

☐ ☐ ☐ ☐ ☐ ☐ ☐ ☐ ☐ ☐ ☐ ☐

Add your favorite ticket stub, postcard, photo, stamp or drawing here

LET NEW ADVENTURES
>> BEGIN →

RED ROCK CANYON STATE PARK

County: Kern

Established: 1970   *Acres:* 25,325

Star Rating
☆☆☆☆☆

My favorite thing about this place is... _____

Why I went ... _____

Who I went with ... _____

When I went ... _____

What I did... _____

What I saw... _____

What I learned... _____

An unforgettable moment... _____

A laughable moment... _____

A surprising moment... _____

An unforeseeable moment... _____

Wildlife spotted... _____

List

- ☐ _____
- ☐ _____
- ☐ _____
- ☐ _____
- ☐ _____
- ☐ _____
- ☐ _____
- ☐ _____
- ☐ _____
- ☐ _____
- ☐ _____
- ☐ _____
- ☐ _____
- ☐ _____
- ☐ _____
- ☐ _____
- ☐ _____
- ☐ _____
- ☐ _____

Snapped a selfie | Location...

Took a park sign photo? - ☐ y ☐ n

The weather was ... ☐ ☐ ☐ ☐ ☐ ☐ ☐

PLAN YOUR TRIP:

☐ Day Trip   ☐ Overnight Stay

Reservations required: ☐ y ☐ n

Date reservations made: _____

Refund Policy: ☐ y ☐ n Site #: _____

Confirmation #: _____

Miles to travel: _____

Time traveling: _____

RV's?: ☐ y ☐ n Largest size RV? _____

Activities Accomplished:

☐ Archery
☐ Biking
☐ Birding
☐ Boating
☐ Camping
☐ Caving
☐ Geocaching

☐ Fishing
☐ Hiking
☐ Horseback Riding
☐ Hunting
☐ Off-Roading
☐ Paddle Boarding
☐ Photography

☐ Picknicking
☐ Rock Climbing
☐ Shooting Range
☐ Snowshoeing
☐ Stargazing
☐ Swimming
☐ Tennis

☐ Walking
☐ Wildlife Watching
☐ _____
☐ _____
☐ _____
☐ _____
☐ _____

Traveling by:

☐ ☐ ☐ ☐ ☐ ☐ ☐ ☐ ☐ ☐ ☐ ☐

RESERVATION INFORMATION:

Address: _____
_____

Reserved dates: _____

Check-in time: _____ Early check-in?: ☐ y ☐ n

Check-out time: _____ Late check-out?: ☐ y ☐ n

Website: _____

Phone: _____

WiFi: _____ WiFi password: _____

Dog friendly?: ☐ y ☐ n   Open all year?: ☐ y ☐ n

Add your favorite ticket stub, postcard, photo, stamp or drawing here

LET NEW ADVENTURES
≫ BEGIN →

Richardson Grove State Park

County: Humboldt

Established: 1922

Acres: 1,772

Star Rating
☆ ☆ ☆ ☆ ☆

My favorite thing about this place is... _____

Why I went ... _____

Who I went with ... _____

When I went ... _____

What I did... _____

What I saw... _____

What I learned... _____

An unforgettable moment... _____

A laughable moment... _____

A surprising moment... _____

An unforeseeable moment... _____

Wildlife spotted... _____

List
- ☐ _____
- ☐ _____
- ☐ _____
- ☐ _____
- ☐ _____
- ☐ _____
- ☐ _____
- ☐ _____
- ☐ _____
- ☐ _____
- ☐ _____
- ☐ _____
- ☐ _____
- ☐ _____
- ☐ _____
- ☐ _____
- ☐ _____
- ☐ _____

Snapped a selfie | Location... _____

Took a park sign photo? - ☐ y ☐ n

The weather was ... ☐ ☐ ☐ ☐ ☐ ☐ ☐

PLAN YOUR TRIP:

RESERVATION INFORMATION:

☐ Day Trip   ☐ Overnight Stay

Reservations required: ☐ y ☐ n

Date reservations made: _____

Refund Policy: ☐ y ☐ n Site #: _____

Confirmation #: _____

Miles to travel: _____

Time traveling: _____

RV's?: ☐ y ☐ n Largest size RV? _____

Address: _____
_____

Reserved dates: _____

Check-in time: _____ Early check-in?: ☐ y ☐ n

Check-out time: _____ Late check-out?: ☐ y ☐ n

Website: _____

Phone: _____

WiFi: _____ WiFi password: _____

Dog friendly?: ☐ y ☐ n   Open all year?: ☐ y ☐ n

Activities Accomplished:

☐ Archery
☐ Biking
☐ Birding
☐ Boating
☐ Camping
☐ Caving
☐ Geocaching

☐ Fishing
☐ Hiking
☐ Horseback Riding
☐ Hunting
☐ Off-Roading
☐ Paddle Boarding
☐ Photography

☐ Picknicking
☐ Rock Climbing
☐ Shooting Range
☐ Snowshoeing
☐ Stargazing
☐ Swimming
☐ Tennis

☐ Walking
☐ Wildlife Watching
☐ _____
☐ _____
☐ _____
☐ _____
☐ _____

Traveling by:

☐ ☐ ☐ ☐ ☐ ☐ ☐ ☐ ☐ ☐ ☐ ☐

Add your favorite ticket stub, postcard, photo, stamp or drawing here

LET NEW ADVENTURES
»» BEGIN →

ROBERT LOUIS STEVENSON STATE PARK

County: Napa, Sonoma, and Lake

Established: 1949   *Acres:* 5,990

Star Rating

☆ ☆ ☆ ☆ ☆

My favorite thing about this place is... _____

Why I went ... _____

Who I went with ... _____

When I went ... _____

What I did... _____

What I saw... _____

What I learned... _____

An unforgettable moment... _____

A laughable moment... _____

A surprising moment... _____

An unforeseeable moment... _____

Wildlife spotted... _____

List

☐ _____
☐ _____
☐ _____
☐ _____
☐ _____
☐ _____
☐ _____
☐ _____
☐ _____
☐ _____
☐ _____
☐ _____
☐ _____
☐ _____
☐ _____
☐ _____
☐ _____
☐ _____

📷 Snapped a selfie | Location... _____

📷 Took a park sign photo? - ☐ y ☐ n

The weather was ...

☐ ☐ ☐ ☐ ☐ ☐ ☐

PLAN YOUR TRIP:

RESERVATION INFORMATION:

☐ Day Trip   ☐ Overnight Stay

Reservations required: ☐ y ☐ n

Date reservations made: _____

Refund Policy: ☐ y ☐ n Site #: _____

Confirmation #: _____

Miles to travel: _____

Time traveling: _____

RV's?: ☐ y ☐ n Largest size RV? _____

Address: _____
_____

Reserved dates: _____

Check-in time: _____ Early check-in?: ☐ y ☐ n

Check-out time: _____ Late check-out?: ☐ y ☐ n

Website: _____

Phone: _____

WiFi: _____ WiFi password: _____

Dog friendly?: ☐ y ☐ n   Open all year?: ☐ y ☐ n

Activities Accomplished:

☐ Archery
☐ Biking
☐ Birding
☐ Boating
☐ Camping
☐ Caving
☐ Geocaching

☐ Fishing
☐ Hiking
☐ Horseback Riding
☐ Hunting
☐ Off-Roading
☐ Paddle Boarding
☐ Photography

☐ Picknicking
☐ Rock Climbing
☐ Shooting Range
☐ Snowshoeing
☐ Stargazing
☐ Swimming
☐ Tennis

☐ Walking
☐ Wildlife Watching
☐ _____
☐ _____
☐ _____
☐ _____
☐ _____

Traveling by:

☐ ☐ ☐ ☐ ☐ ☐ ☐ ☐ ☐ ☐ ☐ ☐

Add your favorite ticket stub, postcard, photo, stamp or drawing here

LET NEW ADVENTURES
≫ BEGIN →

RUSSIAN GULCH STATE PARK

County: Mendocino

Established: 1933

Acres: 1,305

Star Rating
☆☆☆☆☆

My favorite thing about this place is... _____

Why I went ... _____

Who I went with ... _____

When I went ... _____

What I did... _____

What I saw... _____

What I learned... _____

An unforgettable moment... _____

A laughable moment... _____

A surprising moment... _____

An unforeseeable moment... _____

Wildlife spotted... _____

List

☐ _____
☐ _____
☐ _____
☐ _____
☐ _____
☐ _____
☐ _____
☐ _____
☐ _____
☐ _____
☐ _____
☐ _____
☐ _____
☐ _____
☐ _____
☐ _____
☐ _____
☐ _____

📷 Snapped a selfie | Location... _____

📷 Took a park sign photo? - ☐ y ☐ n

The weather was ...
☐ ☐ ☐ ☐ ☐ ☐ ☐

PLAN YOUR TRIP:

☐ Day Trip   ☐ Overnight Stay

Reservations required: ☐ y ☐ n

Date reservations made: _____

Refund Policy: ☐ y ☐ n Site #: _____

Confirmation #: _____

Miles to travel: _____

Time traveling: _____

RV's?: ☐ y ☐ n Largest size RV? _____

Activities Accomplished:

☐ Archery
☐ Biking
☐ Birding
☐ Boating
☐ Camping
☐ Caving
☐ Geocaching

☐ Fishing
☐ Hiking
☐ Horseback Riding
☐ Hunting
☐ Off-Roading
☐ Paddle Boarding
☐ Photography

☐ Picknicking
☐ Rock Climbing
☐ Shooting Range
☐ Snowshoeing
☐ Stargazing
☐ Swimming
☐ Tennis

☐ Walking
☐ Wildlife Watching
☐ _____
☐ _____
☐ _____
☐ _____
☐ _____

Traveling by:

☐ ☐ ☐ ☐ ☐ ☐ ☐ ☐ ☐ ☐ ☐ ☐

RESERVATION INFORMATION:

Address: _____
_____

Reserved dates: _____

Check-in time: _____   Early check-in?: ☐ y ☐ n

Check-out time: _____   Late check-out?: ☐ y ☐ n

Website: _____

Phone: _____

WiFi: _____   WiFi password: _____

Dog friendly?: ☐ y ☐ n   Open all year?: ☐ y ☐ n

Add your favorite ticket stub, postcard, photo, stamp or drawing here

LET NEW ADVENTURES
≫ BEGIN →

Saddleback Butte State Park

County: Los Angeles

Established: 1957

Acres: 2,954

Star Rating
☆ ☆ ☆ ☆ ☆

My favorite thing about this place is... _____

Why I went ... _____

Who I went with ... _____

When I went ... _____

What I did... _____

What I saw... _____

What I learned... _____

An unforgettable moment... _____

A laughable moment... _____

A surprising moment... _____

An unforeseeable moment... _____

Wildlife spotted... _____

List

☐ _____
☐ _____
☐ _____
☐ _____
☐ _____
☐ _____
☐ _____
☐ _____
☐ _____
☐ _____
☐ _____
☐ _____
☐ _____
☐ _____
☐ _____
☐ _____
☐ _____
☐ _____
☐ _____
☐ _____
☐ _____

Snapped a selfie | Location... _____

Took a park sign photo? - ☐ y ☐ n

The weather was ...
☐ ☐ ☐ ☐ ☐ ☐ ☐

PLAN YOUR TRIP:

☐ Day Trip   ☐ Overnight Stay

Reservations required: ☐ y ☐ n

Date reservations made: _____

Refund Policy: ☐ y ☐ n Site #: _____

Confirmation #: _____

Miles to travel: _____

Time traveling: _____

RV's?: ☐ y ☐ n Largest size RV? _____

Activities Accomplished:

☐ Archery
☐ Biking
☐ Birding
☐ Boating
☐ Camping
☐ Caving
☐ Geocaching

☐ Fishing
☐ Hiking
☐ Horseback Riding
☐ Hunting
☐ Off-Roading
☐ Paddle Boarding
☐ Photography

☐ Picknicking
☐ Rock Climbing
☐ Shooting Range
☐ Snowshoeing
☐ Stargazing
☐ Swimming
☐ Tennis

☐ Walking
☐ Wildlife Watching
☐ _____
☐ _____
☐ _____
☐ _____
☐ _____

Traveling by:

☐ ☐ ☐ ☐ ☐ ☐ ☐ ☐ ☐ ☐ ☐ ☐

RESERVATION INFORMATION:

Address: _____
_____

Reserved dates: _____

Check-in time: _____ Early check-in?: ☐ y ☐ n

Check-out time: _____ Late check-out?: ☐ y ☐ n

Website: _____

Phone: _____

WiFi: _____ WiFi password: _____

Dog friendly?: ☐ y ☐ n   Open all year?: ☐ y ☐ n

Add your favorite ticket stub, postcard, photo, stamp or drawing here

LET NEW ADVENTURES
≫ BEGIN →

SALT POINT STATE PARK

County: Sonoma

Established: 1968　　　　　　　　　　　　　　　　　　　　*Acres: 5,684*

Star Rating
☆ ☆ ☆ ☆ ☆

My favorite thing about this place is... _____

Why I went ... _____

Who I went with ... _____

When I went ... _____

What I did... _____

What I saw... _____

What I learned... _____

An unforgettable moment... _____

A laughable moment... _____

A surprising moment... _____

An unforeseeable moment... _____

Wildlife spotted... _____

Snapped a selfie | Location... _____

Took a park sign photo? - ☐ y ☐ n

List
- ☐ _____
- ☐ _____
- ☐ _____
- ☐ _____
- ☐ _____
- ☐ _____
- ☐ _____
- ☐ _____
- ☐ _____
- ☐ _____
- ☐ _____
- ☐ _____
- ☐ _____
- ☐ _____
- ☐ _____
- ☐ _____
- ☐ _____
- ☐ _____

The weather was ... ☐ ☐ ☐ ☐ ☐ ☐ ☐

PLAN YOUR TRIP:

☐ Day Trip   ☐ Overnight Stay

Reservations required: ☐y ☐n

Date reservations made: _____

Refund Policy: ☐y ☐n Site #: _____

Confirmation #: _____

Miles to travel: _____

Time traveling: _____

RV's?: ☐y ☐n Largest size RV? _____

Activities Accomplished:

☐ Archery
☐ Biking
☐ Birding
☐ Boating
☐ Camping
☐ Caving
☐ Geocaching

☐ Fishing
☐ Hiking
☐ Horseback Riding
☐ Hunting
☐ Off-Roading
☐ Paddle Boarding
☐ Photography

☐ Picknicking
☐ Rock Climbing
☐ Shooting Range
☐ Snowshoeing
☐ Stargazing
☐ Swimming
☐ Tennis

☐ Walking
☐ Wildlife Watching
☐ _____
☐ _____
☐ _____
☐ _____
☐ _____

RESERVATION INFORMATION:

Address: _____
_____

Reserved dates: _____

Check-in time: _____ Early check-in?: ☐y ☐n

Check-out time: _____ Late check-out?: ☐y ☐n

Website: _____

Phone: _____

WiFi: _____ WiFi password: _____

Dog friendly?: ☐y ☐n   Open all year?: ☐y ☐n

Traveling by:

☐ ☐ ☐ ☐ ☐ ☐ ☐ ☐ ☐ ☐ ☐ ☐

Add your favorite ticket stub, postcard, photo, stamp or drawing here

LET NEW ADVENTURES
»» BEGIN →

www.mynaturebookadventures.com

Samuel P. Taylor State Park

County: Marin

Established: 1946

Acres: 2,707

Star Rating
☆☆☆☆☆

My favorite thing about this place is... _____

Why I went ... _____

Who I went with ... _____

When I went ... _____

What I did... _____

What I saw... _____

What I learned... _____

An unforgettable moment... _____

A laughable moment... _____

A surprising moment... _____

An unforeseeable moment... _____

Wildlife spotted... _____

Snapped a selfie | Location... _____

Took a park sign photo? - ☐ y ☐ n

The weather was ...

List

☐ _____
☐ _____
☐ _____
☐ _____
☐ _____
☐ _____
☐ _____
☐ _____
☐ _____
☐ _____
☐ _____
☐ _____
☐ _____
☐ _____
☐ _____
☐ _____
☐ _____
☐ _____

PLAN YOUR TRIP:

☐ Day Trip   ☐ Overnight Stay

Reservations required: ☐ y ☐ n

Date reservations made: _____

Refund Policy: ☐ y ☐ n Site #: _____

Confirmation #: _____

Miles to travel: _____

Time traveling: _____

RV's?: ☐ y ☐ n Largest size RV? _____

Activities Accomplished:

☐ Archery
☐ Biking
☐ Birding
☐ Boating
☐ Camping
☐ Caving
☐ Geocaching

☐ Fishing
☐ Hiking
☐ Horseback Riding
☐ Hunting
☐ Off-Roading
☐ Paddle Boarding
☐ Photography

☐ Picknicking
☐ Rock Climbing
☐ Shooting Range
☐ Snowshoeing
☐ Stargazing
☐ Swimming
☐ Tennis

☐ Walking
☐ Wildlife Watching
☐ _____
☐ _____
☐ _____
☐ _____
☐ _____

Traveling by:

☐   ☐   ☐   ☐   ☐   ☐   ☐   ☐   ☐   ☐   ☐   ☐

RESERVATION INFORMATION:

Address: _____
_____

Reserved dates: _____

Check-in time: _____ Early check-in?: ☐ y ☐ n

Check-out time: _____ Late check-out?: ☐ y ☐ n

Website: _____

Phone: _____

WiFi: _____ WiFi password: _____

Dog friendly?: ☐ y ☐ n   Open all year?: ☐ y ☐ n

Add your favorite ticket stub, postcard, photo, stamp or drawing here

LET NEW ADVENTURES
»» BEGIN →

San Bruno Mountain State Park

County: San Mateo

Established: 1980   *Acres:* 298

_____
Star Rating
☆ ☆ ☆ ☆ ☆

My favorite thing about this place is... _____

Why I went ... _____

Who I went with ... _____

When I went ... _____

What I did... _____

What I saw... _____

_____

List

What I learned... _____

- [ ] _____
- [ ] _____
- [ ] _____
- [ ] _____

An unforgettable moment...

- [ ] _____
- [ ] _____
- [ ] _____
- [ ] _____
- [ ] _____

A laughable moment...

- [ ] _____
- [ ] _____
- [ ] _____
- [ ] _____

A surprising moment...

- [ ] _____
- [ ] _____
- [ ] _____
- [ ] _____

An unforeseeable moment...

- [ ] _____
- [ ] _____
- [ ] _____

Wildlife spotted... _____

Snapped a selfie | Location... _____

Took a park sign photo? - ☐ y ☐ n

The weather was ...   ☀ ⛅ 🌧 ⛈ 🌫 ❄ 🌡
☐   ☐   ☐   ☐   ☐   ☐   ☐

PLAN YOUR TRIP:

☐ Day Trip   ☐ Overnight Stay

Reservations required: ☐ y ☐ n

Date reservations made: _____

Refund Policy: ☐ y ☐ n   Site #: _____

Confirmation #: _____

Miles to travel: _____

Time traveling: _____

RV's?: ☐ y ☐ n Largest size RV? _____

Activities Accomplished:

☐ Archery
☐ Biking
☐ Birding
☐ Boating
☐ Camping
☐ Caving
☐ Geocaching

☐ Fishing
☐ Hiking
☐ Horseback Riding
☐ Hunting
☐ Off-Roading
☐ Paddle Boarding
☐ Photography

☐ Picknicking
☐ Rock Climbing
☐ Shooting Range
☐ Snowshoeing
☐ Stargazing
☐ Swimming
☐ Tennis

☐ Walking
☐ Wildlife Watching
☐ _____
☐ _____
☐ _____
☐ _____
☐ _____

RESERVATION INFORMATION:

Address: _____
_____

Reserved dates: _____

Check-in time: _____   Early check-in?: ☐ y ☐ n

Check-out time: _____   Late check-out?: ☐ y ☐ n

Website: _____

Phone: _____

WiFi: _____   WiFi password: _____

Dog friendly?: ☐ y ☐ n   Open all year?: ☐ y ☐ n

Traveling by:

☐ ☐ ☐ ☐ ☐ ☐ ☐ ☐ ☐ ☐ ☐ ☐

Add your favorite ticket stub, postcard, photo, stamp or drawing here

LET NEW ADVENTURES
≫ BEGIN →

SINKYONE WILDERNESS STATE PARK

County: Mendocino and Humboldt

Established: 1975

Acres: 7,937

Star Rating
☆ ☆ ☆ ☆ ☆

My favorite thing about this place is... _____

Why I went ... _____

Who I went with ... _____

When I went ... _____

What I did... _____

What I saw... _____

What I learned... _____

An unforgettable moment... _____

A laughable moment... _____

A surprising moment... _____

An unforeseeable moment... _____

Wildlife spotted... _____

List
- [ ] _____
- [ ] _____
- [ ] _____
- [ ] _____
- [ ] _____
- [ ] _____
- [ ] _____
- [ ] _____
- [ ] _____
- [ ] _____
- [ ] _____
- [ ] _____
- [ ] _____
- [ ] _____
- [ ] _____
- [ ] _____
- [ ] _____
- [ ] _____
- [ ] _____
- [ ] _____

Snapped a selfie | Location... _____

Took a park sign photo? - ☐ y ☐ n

The weather was ...
☐ ☐ ☐ ☐ ☐ ☐ ☐

PLAN YOUR TRIP:

☐ Day Trip   ☐ Overnight Stay

Reservations required: ☐ y ☐ n

Date reservations made: _____

Refund Policy: ☐ y ☐ n Site #: _____

Confirmation #: _____

Miles to travel: _____

Time traveling: _____

RV's?: ☐ y ☐ n Largest size RV? _____

Activities Accomplished:

☐ Archery
☐ Biking
☐ Birding
☐ Boating
☐ Camping
☐ Caving
☐ Geocaching

☐ Fishing
☐ Hiking
☐ Horseback Riding
☐ Hunting
☐ Off-Roading
☐ Paddle Boarding
☐ Photography

☐ Picknicking
☐ Rock Climbing
☐ Shooting Range
☐ Snowshoeing
☐ Stargazing
☐ Swimming
☐ Tennis

☐ Walking
☐ Wildlife Watching
☐ _____
☐ _____
☐ _____
☐ _____
☐ _____

RESERVATION INFORMATION:

Address: _____
_____

Reserved dates: _____

Check-in time: _____ Early check-in?: ☐ y ☐ n

Check-out time: _____ Late check-out?: ☐ y ☐ n

Website: _____

Phone: _____

WiFi: _____ WiFi password: _____

Dog friendly?: ☐ y ☐ n   Open all year?: ☐ y ☐ n

Traveling by:

☐ ☐ ☐ ☐ ☐ ☐ ☐ ☐ ☐ ☐ ☐ ☐

Add your favorite ticket stub, postcard, photo, stamp or drawing here

LET NEW ADVENTURES
»» BEGIN →

SONOMA COAST STATE PARK

County: Sonoma

Established: 1934

Acres: 10,018

Star Rating
☆ ☆ ☆ ☆ ☆

My favorite thing about this place is... _____

Why I went ... _____

Who I went with ... _____

When I went ... _____

What I did... _____

What I saw... _____

What I learned... _____

List

- ☐ _____
- ☐ _____
- ☐ _____
- ☐ _____
- ☐ _____
- ☐ _____
- ☐ _____
- ☐ _____
- ☐ _____
- ☐ _____
- ☐ _____
- ☐ _____
- ☐ _____
- ☐ _____
- ☐ _____
- ☐ _____
- ☐ _____
- ☐ _____
- ☐ _____

An unforgettable moment... _____

A laughable moment... _____

A surprising moment... _____

An unforeseeable moment... _____

Wildlife spotted... _____

Snapped a selfie | Location... _____

Took a park sign photo? - ☐ y ☐ n

The weather was ... ☐ ☐ ☐ ☐ ☐ ☐ ☐

PLAN YOUR TRIP:

☐ Day Trip   ☐ Overnight Stay

Reservations required: ☐ y ☐ n

Date reservations made: _____

Refund Policy: ☐ y ☐ n Site #: _____

Confirmation #: _____

Miles to travel: _____

Time traveling: _____

RV's?: ☐ y ☐ n Largest size RV? _____

Activities Accomplished:

☐ Archery
☐ Biking
☐ Birding
☐ Boating
☐ Camping
☐ Caving
☐ Geocaching

☐ Fishing
☐ Hiking
☐ Horseback Riding
☐ Hunting
☐ Off-Roading
☐ Paddle Boarding
☐ Photography

☐ Picknicking
☐ Rock Climbing
☐ Shooting Range
☐ Snowshoeing
☐ Stargazing
☐ Swimming
☐ Tennis

☐ Walking
☐ Wildlife Watching
☐ _____
☐ _____
☐ _____
☐ _____
☐ _____

RESERVATION INFORMATION:

Address: _____
_____

Reserved dates: _____

Check-in time: _____ Early check-in?: ☐ y ☐ n

Check-out time: _____ Late check-out?: ☐ y ☐ n

Website: _____

Phone: _____

WiFi: _____ WiFi password: _____

Dog friendly?: ☐ y ☐ n   Open all year?: ☐ y ☐ n

Traveling by:

☐ ☐ ☐ ☐ ☐ ☐ ☐ ☐ ☐ ☐ ☐ ☐

Add your favorite ticket stub, postcard, photo, stamp or drawing here

LET NEW ADVENTURES
≫ BEGIN →

South Yuba River State Park

County: Nevada

Established: 1979   *Acres: 8,720*

Star Rating
☆ ☆ ☆ ☆ ☆

My favorite thing about this place is... _____

Why I went ... _____

Who I went with ... _____

When I went ... _____

What I did... _____

What I saw... _____

What I learned... _____

An unforgettable moment... _____

A laughable moment... _____

A surprising moment... _____

An unforeseeable moment... _____

Wildlife spotted... _____

List
- ☐ _____
- ☐ _____
- ☐ _____
- ☐ _____
- ☐ _____
- ☐ _____
- ☐ _____
- ☐ _____
- ☐ _____
- ☐ _____
- ☐ _____
- ☐ _____
- ☐ _____
- ☐ _____
- ☐ _____
- ☐ _____
- ☐ _____
- ☐ _____

Snapped a selfie | Location... _____

Took a park sign photo? - ☐ y ☐ n

The weather was ... ☐ ☐ ☐ ☐ ☐ ☐ ☐

PLAN YOUR TRIP:

☐ Day Trip   ☐ Overnight Stay

Reservations required: ☐ y ☐ n

Date reservations made: _____

Refund Policy: ☐ y ☐ n Site #: _____

Confirmation #: _____

Miles to travel: _____

Time traveling: _____

RV's?: ☐ y ☐ n Largest size RV? _____

Activities Accomplished:

☐ Archery
☐ Biking
☐ Birding
☐ Boating
☐ Camping
☐ Caving
☐ Geocaching

☐ Fishing
☐ Hiking
☐ Horseback Riding
☐ Hunting
☐ Off-Roading
☐ Paddle Boarding
☐ Photography

☐ Picknicking
☐ Rock Climbing
☐ Shooting Range
☐ Snowshoeing
☐ Stargazing
☐ Swimming
☐ Tennis

☐ Walking
☐ Wildlife Watching
☐ _____
☐ _____
☐ _____
☐ _____
☐ _____

RESERVATION INFORMATION:

Address: _____

_____

Reserved dates: _____

Check-in time: _____ Early check-in?: ☐ y ☐ n

Check-out time: _____ Late check-out?: ☐ y ☐ n

Website: _____

Phone: _____

WiFi: _____ WiFi password: _____

Dog friendly?: ☐ y ☐ n   Open all year?: ☐ y ☐ n

Traveling by:

☐ ☐ ☐ ☐ ☐ ☐ ☐ ☐ ☐ ☐ ☐ ☐

Add your favorite ticket stub, postcard, photo, stamp or drawing here

LET NEW ADVENTURES
≫ BEGIN →

Sugarloaf Ridge State Park

County: Sonoma and Napa

Established: 1920   *Acres:* 4,416

Managed by a group of Sonoma County non-profits as Team Sugarloaf with no state funding.

Star Rating
☆ ☆ ☆ ☆ ☆

My favorite thing about this place is... _____

Why I went ... _____

Who I went with ... _____

When I went ... _____

What I did... _____

What I saw... _____

What I learned... _____

An unforgettable moment... _____

A laughable moment... _____

A surprising moment... _____

An unforeseeable moment... _____

Wildlife spotted... _____

List
- ☐ _____
- ☐ _____
- ☐ _____
- ☐ _____
- ☐ _____
- ☐ _____
- ☐ _____
- ☐ _____
- ☐ _____
- ☐ _____
- ☐ _____
- ☐ _____
- ☐ _____
- ☐ _____
- ☐ _____
- ☐ _____
- ☐ _____
- ☐ _____
- ☐ _____

Snapped a selfie | Location...

Took a park sign photo? - ☐ y ☐ n

The weather was ... ☐ ☐ ☐ ☐ ☐ ☐ ☐

PLAN YOUR TRIP:

RESERVATION INFORMATION:

☐ Day Trip   ☐ Overnight Stay

Reservations required: ☐ y ☐ n

Date reservations made: _____

Refund Policy: ☐ y ☐ n Site #: _____

Confirmation #: _____

Miles to travel: _____

Time traveling: _____

RV's?: ☐ y ☐ n Largest size RV? _____

Address: _____
_____

Reserved dates: _____

Check-in time: _____ Early check-in?: ☐ y ☐ n

Check-out time: _____ Late check-out?: ☐ y ☐ n

Website: _____

Phone: _____

WiFi: _____ WiFi password: _____

Dog friendly?: ☐ y ☐ n   Open all year?: ☐ y ☐ n

Activities Accomplished:

☐ Archery
☐ Biking
☐ Birding
☐ Boating
☐ Camping
☐ Caving
☐ Geocaching

☐ Fishing
☐ Hiking
☐ Horseback Riding
☐ Hunting
☐ Off-Roading
☐ Paddle Boarding
☐ Photography

☐ Picknicking
☐ Rock Climbing
☐ Shooting Range
☐ Snowshoeing
☐ Stargazing
☐ Swimming
☐ Tennis

☐ Walking
☐ Wildlife Watching
☐ _____
☐ _____
☐ _____
☐ _____
☐ _____

Traveling by:

☐ ☐ ☐ ☐ ☐ ☐ ☐ ☐ ☐ ☐ ☐ ☐

Add your favorite ticket stub, postcard, photo, stamp or drawing here

LET NEW ADVENTURES
»» BEGIN →

SUTTER BUTTES STATE PARK

County: Sutter

Established: *2003*   *Acres: 1,785*

In development on the north side of the Sutter Buttes. This park has not officially been named but has been classified as a state park. The use of Sutter Buttes in the name was allowed temporarily by the California State Parks Commission in 2004. Currently no public access.

Star Rating
☆ ☆ ☆ ☆ ☆

My favorite thing about this place is... _____

Why I went ... _____

Who I went with ... _____

When I went ... _____

What I did... _____

What I saw... _____

What I learned... _____

An unforgettable moment... _____

A laughable moment... _____

A surprising moment... _____

An unforeseeable moment... _____

Wildlife spotted... _____

List
- ☐ _____
- ☐ _____
- ☐ _____
- ☐ _____
- ☐ _____
- ☐ _____
- ☐ _____
- ☐ _____
- ☐ _____
- ☐ _____
- ☐ _____
- ☐ _____
- ☐ _____
- ☐ _____
- ☐ _____
- ☐ _____
- ☐ _____
- ☐ _____

Snapped a selfie | Location...

Took a park sign photo? - ☐ y ☐ n

The weather was ... ☐ ☐ ☐ ☐ ☐ ☐ ☐

PLAN YOUR TRIP:

☐ Day Trip   ☐ Overnight Stay

Reservations required: ☐ y ☐ n

Date reservations made: _____

Refund Policy: ☐ y ☐ n Site #: _____

Confirmation #: _____

Miles to travel: _____

Time traveling: _____

RV's?: ☐ y ☐ n Largest size RV? _____

Activities Accomplished:

☐ Archery
☐ Biking
☐ Birding
☐ Boating
☐ Camping
☐ Caving
☐ Geocaching

☐ Fishing
☐ Hiking
☐ Horseback Riding
☐ Hunting
☐ Off-Roading
☐ Paddle Boarding
☐ Photography

☐ Picknicking
☐ Rock Climbing
☐ Shooting Range
☐ Snowshoeing
☐ Stargazing
☐ Swimming
☐ Tennis

☐ Walking
☐ Wildlife Watching
☐ _____
☐ _____
☐ _____
☐ _____
☐ _____

RESERVATION INFORMATION:

Address: _____
_____

Reserved dates: _____

Check-in time: _____ Early check-in?: ☐ y ☐ n

Check-out time: _____ Late check-out?: ☐ y ☐ n

Website: _____

Phone: _____

WiFi: _____ WiFi password: _____

Dog friendly?: ☐ y ☐ n   Open all year?: ☐ y ☐ n

Traveling by:

☐   ☐   ☐   ☐   ☐   ☐   ☐   ☐   ☐   ☐   ☐   ☐

Add your favorite ticket stub, postcard, photo, stamp or drawing here

LET NEW ADVENTURES
≫ BEGIN →

Tolowa Dunes State Park

County: Del Norte

Established: 1983

Acres: 4,399

Star Rating

☆ ☆ ☆ ☆ ☆

My favorite thing about this place is... _____

Why I went ... _____

Who I went with ... _____

When I went ... _____

What I did... _____

What I saw... _____

What I learned... _____

An unforgettable moment... _____

A laughable moment... _____

A surprising moment... _____

An unforeseeable moment... _____

Wildlife spotted... _____

Snapped a selfie | Location... _____

Took a park sign photo? - ☐ y ☐ n

List

☐ _____
☐ _____
☐ _____
☐ _____
☐ _____
☐ _____
☐ _____
☐ _____
☐ _____
☐ _____
☐ _____
☐ _____
☐ _____
☐ _____
☐ _____
☐ _____
☐ _____
☐ _____
☐ _____

The weather was ...

☐ ☐ ☐ ☐ ☐ ☐ ☐

PLAN YOUR TRIP:

☐ Day Trip   ☐ Overnight Stay

Reservations required: ☐ y ☐ n

Date reservations made: _____

Refund Policy: ☐ y ☐ n Site #: _____

Confirmation #: _____

Miles to travel: _____

Time traveling: _____

RV's?: ☐ y ☐ n Largest size RV? _____

Activities Accomplished:

☐ Archery
☐ Biking
☐ Birding
☐ Boating
☐ Camping
☐ Caving
☐ Geocaching

☐ Fishing
☐ Hiking
☐ Horseback Riding
☐ Hunting
☐ Off-Roading
☐ Paddle Boarding
☐ Photography

☐ Picknicking
☐ Rock Climbing
☐ Shooting Range
☐ Snowshoeing
☐ Stargazing
☐ Swimming
☐ Tennis

☐ Walking
☐ Wildlife Watching
☐ _____
☐ _____
☐ _____
☐ _____
☐ _____

Traveling by:

☐ ☐ ☐ ☐ ☐ ☐ ☐ ☐ ☐ ☐ ☐ ☐

RESERVATION INFORMATION:

Address: _____
_____

Reserved dates: _____

Check-in time: _____ Early check-in?: ☐ y ☐ n

Check-out time: _____ Late check-out?: ☐ y ☐ n

Website: _____

Phone: _____

WiFi: _____ WiFi password: _____

Dog friendly?: ☐ y ☐ n   Open all year?: ☐ y ☐ n

Add your favorite ticket stub, postcard, photo, stamp or drawing here

LET NEW ADVENTURES
>>> BEGIN →

TOMALES BAY STATE PARK

County: Marin

Established: 1950

Acres: 2,443

Open under National Park Service management

Star Rating
☆ ☆ ☆ ☆ ☆

My favorite thing about this place is... _____

Why I went ... _____

Who I went with ... _____

When I went ... _____

What I did... _____

What I saw... _____

What I learned... _____

An unforgettable moment... _____

A laughable moment... _____

A surprising moment... _____

An unforeseeable moment... _____

Wildlife spotted... _____

List
- [ ] _____
- [ ] _____
- [ ] _____
- [ ] _____
- [ ] _____
- [ ] _____
- [ ] _____
- [ ] _____
- [ ] _____
- [ ] _____
- [ ] _____
- [ ] _____
- [ ] _____
- [ ] _____
- [ ] _____

Snapped a selfie | Location... _____

Took a park sign photo? - ☐ y ☐ n

The weather was ... ☐ ☐ ☐ ☐ ☐ ☐ ☐

PLAN YOUR TRIP:

☐ Day Trip   ☐ Overnight Stay

Reservations required: ☐ y ☐ n

Date reservations made: _____

Refund Policy: ☐ y ☐ n Site #: _____

Confirmation #: _____

Miles to travel: _____

Time traveling: _____

RV's?: ☐ y ☐ n Largest size RV? _____

Activities Accomplished:

☐ Archery
☐ Biking
☐ Birding
☐ Boating
☐ Camping
☐ Caving
☐ Geocaching

☐ Fishing
☐ Hiking
☐ Horseback Riding
☐ Hunting
☐ Off-Roading
☐ Paddle Boarding
☐ Photography

☐ Picknicking
☐ Rock Climbing
☐ Shooting Range
☐ Snowshoeing
☐ Stargazing
☐ Swimming
☐ Tennis

☐ Walking
☐ Wildlife Watching
☐ _____
☐ _____
☐ _____
☐ _____
☐ _____

Traveling by:

☐ ☐ ☐ ☐ ☐ ☐ ☐ ☐ ☐ ☐ ☐ ☐

RESERVATION INFORMATION:

Address: _____
_____

Reserved dates: _____

Check-in time: _____ Early check-in?: ☐ y ☐ n

Check-out time: _____ Late check-out?: ☐ y ☐ n

Website: _____

Phone: _____

WiFi: _____ WiFi password: _____

Dog friendly?: ☐ y ☐ n   Open all year?: ☐ y ☐ n

Add your favorite ticket stub, postcard, photo, stamp or drawing here

LET NEW ADVENTURES
>> BEGIN →

Topanga State Park

County: Los Angeles

Established: 1967   *Acres:* 12,666

Star Rating
☆ ☆ ☆ ☆ ☆

My favorite thing about this place is... _____

Why I went ... _____

Who I went with ... _____

When I went ... _____

What I did... _____

What I saw... _____

_____

What I learned... _____

_____

An unforgettable moment... _____

_____

_____

A laughable moment... _____

_____

A surprising moment... _____

_____

An unforeseeable moment... _____

_____

Wildlife spotted... _____

📷 Snapped a selfie | Location... _____

📷 Took a park sign photo? - ☐ y ☐ n

List

☐ _____
☐ _____
☐ _____
☐ _____
☐ _____
☐ _____
☐ _____
☐ _____
☐ _____
☐ _____
☐ _____
☐ _____
☐ _____
☐ _____
☐ _____
☐ _____
☐ _____
☐ _____
☐ _____
☐ _____

The weather was ...
☐ ☐ ☐ ☐ ☐ ☐ ☐

PLAN YOUR TRIP:

☐ Day Trip   ☐ Overnight Stay

Reservations required: ☐ y ☐ n

Date reservations made: _____

Refund Policy: ☐ y ☐ n Site #: _____

Confirmation #: _____

Miles to travel: _____

Time traveling: _____

RV's?: ☐ y ☐ n Largest size RV? _____

Activities Accomplished:

☐ Archery
☐ Biking
☐ Birding
☐ Boating
☐ Camping
☐ Caving
☐ Geocaching

☐ Fishing
☐ Hiking
☐ Horseback Riding
☐ Hunting
☐ Off-Roading
☐ Paddle Boarding
☐ Photography

☐ Picknicking
☐ Rock Climbing
☐ Shooting Range
☐ Snowshoeing
☐ Stargazing
☐ Swimming
☐ Tennis

☐ Walking
☐ Wildlife Watching
☐ _____
☐ _____
☐ _____
☐ _____
☐ _____

RESERVATION INFORMATION:

Address: _____
_____

Reserved dates: _____

Check-in time: _____ Early check-in?: ☐ y ☐ n

Check-out time: _____ Late check-out?: ☐ y ☐ n

Website: _____

Phone: _____

WiFi: _____ WiFi password: _____

Dog friendly?: ☐ y ☐ n   Open all year?: ☐ y ☐ n

Traveling by:

☐ ☐ ☐ ☐ ☐ ☐ ☐ ☐ ☐ ☐ ☐ ☐

Add your favorite ticket stub, postcard, photo, stamp or drawing here

LET NEW ADVENTURES
≫ BEGIN →

Trione-Annadel State Park

County: Sonoma

Established: 1971   *Acres: 5,092*

Supports a variety of day-use activities at the northern end of Sonoma Valley.

Star Rating

☆ ☆ ☆ ☆ ☆

My favorite thing about this place is... _____

Why I went ... _____

Who I went with ... _____

When I went ... _____

What I did... _____

What I saw... _____

What I learned... _____

List

- [ ] _____
- [ ] _____
- [ ] _____
- [ ] _____
- [ ] _____
- [ ] _____
- [ ] _____
- [ ] _____
- [ ] _____
- [ ] _____
- [ ] _____
- [ ] _____
- [ ] _____
- [ ] _____
- [ ] _____
- [ ] _____
- [ ] _____
- [ ] _____
- [ ] _____
- [ ] _____
- [ ] _____
- [ ] _____

An unforgettable moment... _____

A laughable moment... _____

A surprising moment... _____

An unforeseeable moment... _____

Wildlife spotted... _____

Snapped a selfie | Location... _____

Took a park sign photo? - ☐ y ☐ n

The weather was ... ☐ ☐ ☐ ☐ ☐ ☐ ☐

PLAN YOUR TRIP:

☐ Day Trip   ☐ Overnight Stay

Reservations required: ☐ y ☐ n

Date reservations made: _____

Refund Policy: ☐ y ☐ n   Site #: _____

Confirmation #: _____

Miles to travel: _____

Time traveling: _____

RV's?: ☐ y ☐ n Largest size RV? _____

Activities Accomplished:

☐ Archery
☐ Biking
☐ Birding
☐ Boating
☐ Camping
☐ Caving
☐ Geocaching

☐ Fishing
☐ Hiking
☐ Horseback Riding
☐ Hunting
☐ Off-Roading
☐ Paddle Boarding
☐ Photography

☐ Picknicking
☐ Rock Climbing
☐ Shooting Range
☐ Snowshoeing
☐ Stargazing
☐ Swimming
☐ Tennis

☐ Walking
☐ Wildlife Watching
☐ _____
☐ _____
☐ _____
☐ _____
☐ _____

Traveling by:

☐ ☐ ☐ ☐ ☐ ☐ ☐ ☐ ☐ ☐ ☐ ☐

RESERVATION INFORMATION:

Address: _____
_____

Reserved dates: _____

Check-in time: _____   Early check-in?: ☐ y ☐ n

Check-out time: _____   Late check-out?: ☐ y ☐ n

Website: _____

Phone: _____

WiFi: _____   WiFi password: _____

Dog friendly?: ☐ y ☐ n   Open all year?: ☐ y ☐ n

Add your favorite ticket stub, postcard, photo, stamp or drawing here

LET NEW ADVENTURES
»» BEGIN →

Van Damme State Park

County: Mendocino

Established: 1932   *Acres: 2,336*

Preserves beach, bog, and a pygmy forest on the site of a former redwood lumbering settlement. [138] The pygmy forest is a National Natural Landmark.

Star Rating
☆ ☆ ☆ ☆ ☆

My favorite thing about this place is... _____

Why I went ... _____

Who I went with ... _____

When I went ... _____

What I did... _____

What I saw... _____

What I learned... _____

An unforgettable moment... _____

A laughable moment... _____

A surprising moment... _____

An unforeseeable moment... _____

Wildlife spotted... _____

Snapped a selfie | Location... _____

Took a park sign photo? - ☐ y ☐ n

List
- ☐ _____
- ☐ _____
- ☐ _____
- ☐ _____
- ☐ _____
- ☐ _____
- ☐ _____
- ☐ _____
- ☐ _____
- ☐ _____
- ☐ _____
- ☐ _____
- ☐ _____
- ☐ _____
- ☐ _____
- ☐ _____
- ☐ _____
- ☐ _____

The weather was ...
☐ ☐ ☐ ☐ ☐ ☐ ☐

PLAN YOUR TRIP:

☐ Day Trip ☐ Overnight Stay

Reservations required: ☐ y ☐ n

Date reservations made: _____

Refund Policy: ☐ y ☐ n Site #: _____

Confirmation #: _____

Miles to travel: _____

Time traveling: _____

RV's?: ☐ y ☐ n Largest size RV? _____

Activities Accomplished:

☐ Archery
☐ Biking
☐ Birding
☐ Boating
☐ Camping
☐ Caving
☐ Geocaching

☐ Fishing
☐ Hiking
☐ Horseback Riding
☐ Hunting
☐ Off-Roading
☐ Paddle Boarding
☐ Photography

☐ Picknicking
☐ Rock Climbing
☐ Shooting Range
☐ Snowshoeing
☐ Stargazing
☐ Swimming
☐ Tennis

☐ Walking
☐ Wildlife Watching
☐ _____
☐ _____
☐ _____
☐ _____
☐ _____

RESERVATION INFORMATION:

Address: _____
_____

Reserved dates: _____

Check-in time: _____ Early check-in?: ☐ y ☐ n

Check-out time: _____ Late check-out?: ☐ y ☐ n

Website: _____

Phone: _____

WiFi: _____ WiFi password: _____

Dog friendly?: ☐ y ☐ n Open all year?: ☐ y ☐ n

Traveling by:

☐ ☐ ☐ ☐ ☐ ☐ ☐ ☐ ☐ ☐ ☐ ☐

Add your favorite ticket stub, postcard, photo, stamp or drawing here

LET NEW ADVENTURES
»» BEGIN →

Washoe Meadows State Park

County: El Dorado

Established: 1985

Acres: 628

Star Rating
☆ ☆ ☆ ☆ ☆

My favorite thing about this place is... _____

Why I went ... _____

Who I went with ... _____

When I went ... _____

What I did... _____

What I saw... _____

What I learned... _____

An unforgettable moment... _____

A laughable moment... _____

A surprising moment... _____

An unforeseeable moment... _____

Wildlife spotted... _____

Snapped a selfie | Location...

Took a park sign photo? - ☐ y ☐ n

List

☐ _____
☐ _____
☐ _____
☐ _____
☐ _____
☐ _____
☐ _____
☐ _____
☐ _____
☐ _____
☐ _____
☐ _____
☐ _____
☐ _____
☐ _____
☐ _____
☐ _____
☐ _____

The weather was ...
☐ ☐ ☐ ☐ ☐ ☐ ☐

PLAN YOUR TRIP:

☐ Day Trip   ☐ Overnight Stay

Reservations required: ☐ y ☐ n

Date reservations made: _____

Refund Policy: ☐ y ☐ n   Site #: _____

Confirmation #: _____

Miles to travel: _____

Time traveling: _____

RV's?: ☐ y ☐ n Largest size RV? _____

Activities Accomplished:

☐ Archery
☐ Biking
☐ Birding
☐ Boating
☐ Camping
☐ Caving
☐ Geocaching

☐ Fishing
☐ Hiking
☐ Horseback Riding
☐ Hunting
☐ Off-Roading
☐ Paddle Boarding
☐ Photography

☐ Picknicking
☐ Rock Climbing
☐ Shooting Range
☐ Snowshoeing
☐ Stargazing
☐ Swimming
☐ Tennis

☐ Walking
☐ Wildlife Watching
☐ _____
☐ _____
☐ _____
☐ _____
☐ _____

Traveling by:

☐ ☐ ☐ ☐ ☐ ☐ ☐ ☐ ☐ ☐ ☐ ☐

RESERVATION INFORMATION:

Address: _____
_____

Reserved dates: _____

Check-in time: _____   Early check-in?: ☐ y ☐ n

Check-out time: _____   Late check-out?: ☐ y ☐ n

Website: _____

Phone: _____

WiFi: _____   WiFi password: _____

Dog friendly?: ☐ y ☐ n   Open all year?: ☐ y ☐ n

Add your favorite ticket stub, postcard, photo, stamp or drawing here

LET NEW ADVENTURES
≫ BEGIN →

WILDER RANCH STATE PARK

County: Santa Cruz

Established: 1974

Acres: 8,342

Star Rating

☆☆☆☆☆

My favorite thing about this place is... _____

Why I went ... _____

Who I went with ... _____

When I went ... _____

What I did... _____

What I saw... _____

What I learned... _____

An unforgettable moment... _____

A laughable moment... _____

A surprising moment... _____

An unforeseeable moment... _____

Wildlife spotted... _____

List

- ☐ _____
- ☐ _____
- ☐ _____
- ☐ _____
- ☐ _____
- ☐ _____
- ☐ _____
- ☐ _____
- ☐ _____
- ☐ _____
- ☐ _____
- ☐ _____
- ☐ _____
- ☐ _____
- ☐ _____
- ☐ _____
- ☐ _____
- ☐ _____
- ☐ _____
- ☐ _____

Snapped a selfie | Location... _____

Took a park sign photo? - ☐ y ☐ n

The weather was ... ☐ ☐ ☐ ☐ ☐ ☐ ☐

PLAN YOUR TRIP:

☐ Day Trip   ☐ Overnight Stay

Reservations required: ☐ y ☐ n

Date reservations made: _____

Refund Policy: ☐ y ☐ n Site #: _____

Confirmation #: _____

Miles to travel: _____

Time traveling: _____

RV's?: ☐ y ☐ n Largest size RV? _____

Activities Accomplished:

☐ Archery
☐ Biking
☐ Birding
☐ Boating
☐ Camping
☐ Caving
☐ Geocaching

☐ Fishing
☐ Hiking
☐ Horseback Riding
☐ Hunting
☐ Off-Roading
☐ Paddle Boarding
☐ Photography

☐ Picknicking
☐ Rock Climbing
☐ Shooting Range
☐ Snowshoeing
☐ Stargazing
☐ Swimming
☐ Tennis

☐ Walking
☐ Wildlife Watching
☐ _____
☐ _____
☐ _____
☐ _____
☐ _____

Traveling by:

☐ ☐ ☐ ☐ ☐ ☐ ☐ ☐ ☐ ☐ ☐ ☐

RESERVATION INFORMATION:

Address: _____
_____

Reserved dates: _____

Check-in time: _____ Early check-in?: ☐ y ☐ n

Check-out time: _____ Late check-out?: ☐ y ☐ n

Website: _____

Phone: _____

WiFi: _____ WiFi password: _____

Dog friendly?: ☐ y ☐ n   Open all year?: ☐ y ☐ n

Add your favorite ticket stub, postcard, photo, stamp or drawing here

LET NEW ADVENTURES
≫ BEGIN →

Asilomar State Beach

County: Monterey

Established: 1951

Acres: 107

Balances protection of rocky coast and dune habitat with public access.[13] The 1913 Asilomar Conference Grounds are a National Historic Landmark.

Star Rating

☆ ☆ ☆ ☆ ☆

My favorite thing about this place is... _____

Why I went ... _____

Who I went with ... _____

When I went ... _____

What I did... _____

What I saw... _____

What I learned... _____

An unforgettable moment... _____

A laughable moment... _____

A surprising moment... _____

An unforeseeable moment... _____

Wildlife spotted... _____

List

☐ _____
☐ _____
☐ _____
☐ _____
☐ _____
☐ _____
☐ _____
☐ _____
☐ _____
☐ _____
☐ _____
☐ _____
☐ _____
☐ _____
☐ _____
☐ _____
☐ _____
☐ _____

Snapped a selfie | Location... _____

Took a park sign photo? - ☐ y ☐ n

The weather was ...

☐ ☐ ☐ ☐ ☐ ☐ ☐

PLAN YOUR TRIP:

☐ Day Trip   ☐ Overnight Stay

Reservations required: ☐ y ☐ n

Date reservations made: _____

Refund Policy: ☐ y ☐ n   Site #: _____

Confirmation #: _____

Miles to travel: _____

Time traveling: _____

RV's?: ☐ y ☐ n Largest size RV? _____

Activities Accomplished:

☐ Archery
☐ Biking
☐ Birding
☐ Boating
☐ Camping
☐ Caving
☐ Geocaching

☐ Fishing
☐ Hiking
☐ Horseback Riding
☐ Hunting
☐ Off-Roading
☐ Paddle Boarding
☐ Photography

☐ Picknicking
☐ Rock Climbing
☐ Shooting Range
☐ Snowshoeing
☐ Stargazing
☐ Swimming
☐ Tennis

☐ Walking
☐ Wildlife Watching
☐ _____
☐ _____
☐ _____
☐ _____
☐ _____

RESERVATION INFORMATION:

Address: _____
_____

Reserved dates: _____

Check-in time: _____   Early check-in?: ☐ y ☐ n

Check-out time: _____   Late check-out?: ☐ y ☐ n

Website: _____

Phone: _____

WiFi: _____   WiFi password: _____

Dog friendly?: ☐ y ☐ n   Open all year?: ☐ y ☐ n

Traveling by:

☐ ☐ ☐ ☐ ☐ ☐ ☐ ☐ ☐ ☐ ☐ ☐

Add your favorite ticket stub, postcard, photo, stamp or drawing here

LET NEW ADVENTURES
» BEGIN →

Bean Hollow State Beach

County: San Mateo

Established: 1958

Acres: 44

Offers fishing and beachcombing among tide pools.

Star Rating

☆☆☆☆☆

My favorite thing about this place is... _____

Why I went ... _____

Who I went with ... _____

When I went ... _____

What I did... _____

What I saw... _____

What I learned... _____

An unforgettable moment... _____

A laughable moment... _____

A surprising moment... _____

An unforeseeable moment... _____

Wildlife spotted... _____

List

- [ ] _____
- [ ] _____
- [ ] _____
- [ ] _____
- [ ] _____
- [ ] _____
- [ ] _____
- [ ] _____
- [ ] _____
- [ ] _____
- [ ] _____
- [ ] _____
- [ ] _____
- [ ] _____
- [ ] _____
- [ ] _____
- [ ] _____
- [ ] _____
- [ ] _____
- [ ] _____

Snapped a selfie | Location... _____

Took a park sign photo? - ☐ y ☐ n

The weather was ...

☐ ☐ ☐ ☐ ☐ ☐ ☐

PLAN YOUR TRIP:

☐ Day Trip   ☐ Overnight Stay

Reservations required: ☐ y ☐ n

Date reservations made: _____

Refund Policy: ☐ y ☐ n Site #: _____

Confirmation #: _____

Miles to travel: _____

Time traveling: _____

RV's?: ☐ y ☐ n Largest size RV? _____

Activities Accomplished:

☐ Archery
☐ Biking
☐ Birding
☐ Boating
☐ Camping
☐ Caving
☐ Geocaching

☐ Fishing
☐ Hiking
☐ Horseback Riding
☐ Hunting
☐ Off-Roading
☐ Paddle Boarding
☐ Photography

☐ Picknicking
☐ Rock Climbing
☐ Shooting Range
☐ Snowshoeing
☐ Stargazing
☐ Swimming
☐ Tennis

☐ Walking
☐ Wildlife Watching
☐ _____
☐ _____
☐ _____
☐ _____
☐ _____

Traveling by:

☐ ☐ ☐ ☐ ☐ ☐ ☐ ☐ ☐ ☐ ☐ ☐

RESERVATION INFORMATION:

Address: _____
_____

Reserved dates: _____

Check-in time: _____ Early check-in?: ☐ y ☐ n

Check-out time: _____ Late check-out?: ☐ y ☐ n

Website: _____

Phone: _____

WiFi: _____ WiFi password: _____

Dog friendly?: ☐ y ☐ n   Open all year?: ☐ y ☐ n

Add your favorite ticket stub, postcard, photo, stamp or drawing here

LET NEW ADVENTURES
»» BEGIN →

Bolsa Chica State Beach

County: Orange

Established: 1960

Acres: 169

Offers surf fishing and catching grunion by hand.

Star Rating
☆ ☆ ☆ ☆ ☆

My favorite thing about this place is... _____

Why I went ... _____

Who I went with ... _____

When I went ... _____

What I did... _____

What I saw... _____

What I learned... _____

An unforgettable moment... _____

A laughable moment... _____

A surprising moment... _____

An unforeseeable moment... _____

Wildlife spotted... _____

📷 Snapped a selfie | Location... _____

📷 Took a park sign photo? - ☐ y ☐ n

List

☐ _____
☐ _____
☐ _____
☐ _____
☐ _____
☐ _____
☐ _____
☐ _____
☐ _____
☐ _____
☐ _____
☐ _____
☐ _____
☐ _____
☐ _____
☐ _____
☐ _____
☐ _____
☐ _____

The weather was ...
☐ ☐ ☐ ☐ ☐ ☐ ☐

PLAN YOUR TRIP:

RESERVATION INFORMATION:

☐ Day Trip   ☐ Overnight Stay

Reservations required: ☐ y ☐ n

Date reservations made: _____

Refund Policy: ☐ y ☐ n Site #: _____

Confirmation #: _____

Miles to travel: _____

Time traveling: _____

RV's?: ☐ y ☐ n Largest size RV? _____

Address: _____
_____

Reserved dates: _____

Check-in time: _____ Early check-in?: ☐ y ☐ n

Check-out time: _____ Late check-out?: ☐ y ☐ n

Website: _____

Phone: _____

WiFi: _____ WiFi password: _____

Dog friendly?: ☐ y ☐ n   Open all year?: ☐ y ☐ n

Activities Accomplished:

☐ Archery
☐ Biking
☐ Birding
☐ Boating
☐ Camping
☐ Caving
☐ Geocaching

☐ Fishing
☐ Hiking
☐ Horseback Riding
☐ Hunting
☐ Off-Roading
☐ Paddle Boarding
☐ Photography

☐ Picknicking
☐ Rock Climbing
☐ Shooting Range
☐ Snowshoeing
☐ Stargazing
☐ Swimming
☐ Tennis

☐ Walking
☐ Wildlife Watching
☐ _____
☐ _____
☐ _____
☐ _____
☐ _____

Traveling by:

☐ ☐ ☐ ☐ ☐ ☐ ☐ ☐ ☐ ☐ ☐ ☐

Add your favorite ticket stub, postcard, photo, stamp or drawing here

LET NEW ADVENTURES
≫ BEGIN →

Cardiff State Beach

County: San Diego

Established: 1949

Acres: 507

Provides a sandy, warm-water beach outside San Diego.

Star Rating

☆ ☆ ☆ ☆ ☆

My favorite thing about this place is... _____

Why I went ... _____

Who I went with ... _____

When I went ... _____

What I did... _____

What I saw... _____

What I learned... _____

An unforgettable moment... _____

A laughable moment... _____

A surprising moment... _____

An unforeseeable moment... _____

Wildlife spotted... _____

📷 Snapped a selfie | Location... _____

📷 Took a park sign photo? - ☐ y ☐ n

List

☐ _____
☐ _____
☐ _____
☐ _____
☐ _____
☐ _____
☐ _____
☐ _____
☐ _____
☐ _____
☐ _____
☐ _____
☐ _____
☐ _____
☐ _____
☐ _____
☐ _____
☐ _____

The weather was ... ☐ ☐ ☐ ☐ ☐ ☐ ☐

PLAN YOUR TRIP:

☐ Day Trip   ☐ Overnight Stay

Reservations required: ☐ y ☐ n

Date reservations made: _____

Refund Policy: ☐ y ☐ n   Site #: _____

Confirmation #: _____

Miles to travel: _____

Time traveling: _____

RV's?: ☐ y ☐ n Largest size RV? _____

Activities Accomplished:

☐ Archery
☐ Biking
☐ Birding
☐ Boating
☐ Camping
☐ Caving
☐ Geocaching

☐ Fishing
☐ Hiking
☐ Horseback Riding
☐ Hunting
☐ Off-Roading
☐ Paddle Boarding
☐ Photography

☐ Picknicking
☐ Rock Climbing
☐ Shooting Range
☐ Snowshoeing
☐ Stargazing
☐ Swimming
☐ Tennis

☐ Walking
☐ Wildlife Watching
☐ _____
☐ _____
☐ _____
☐ _____
☐ _____

RESERVATION INFORMATION:

Address: _____
_____

Reserved dates: _____

Check-in time: _____   Early check-in?: ☐ y ☐ n

Check-out time: _____   Late check-out?: ☐ y ☐ n

Website: _____

Phone: _____

WiFi: _____   WiFi password: _____

Dog friendly?: ☐ y ☐ n   Open all year?: ☐ y ☐ n

Traveling by:

☐ ☐ ☐ ☐ ☐ ☐ ☐ ☐ ☐ ☐ ☐ ☐

Add your favorite ticket stub, postcard, photo, stamp or drawing here

LET NEW ADVENTURES
»» BEGIN →

CARLSBAD STATE BEACH

County: San Diego

Established: 1933

Features a small beach at the foot of coastal bluffs.

Acres: 44

Star Rating

☆☆☆☆☆

My favorite thing about this place is...

Why I went ...

Who I went with ...

When I went ...

What I did...

What I saw...

What I learned...

An unforgettable moment...

A laughable moment...

A surprising moment...

An unforeseeable moment...

Wildlife spotted...

List

- [ ]
- [ ]
- [ ]
- [ ]
- [ ]
- [ ]
- [ ]
- [ ]
- [ ]
- [ ]
- [ ]
- [ ]
- [ ]
- [ ]
- [ ]
- [ ]
- [ ]
- [ ]
- [ ]
- [ ]
- [ ]

Snapped a selfie | Location...

Took a park sign photo? - ☐ y ☐ n

The weather was ...

PLAN YOUR TRIP:

RESERVATION INFORMATION:

☐ Day Trip   ☐ Overnight Stay

Reservations required: ☐ y ☐ n

Date reservations made: _____

Refund Policy: ☐ y ☐ n Site #: _____

Confirmation #: _____

Miles to travel: _____

Time traveling: _____

RV's?: ☐ y ☐ n Largest size RV? _____

Address: _____
_____

Reserved dates: _____

Check-in time: _____ Early check-in?: ☐ y ☐ n

Check-out time: _____ Late check-out?: ☐ y ☐ n

Website: _____

Phone: _____

WiFi: _____ WiFi password: _____

Dog friendly?: ☐ y ☐ n   Open all year?: ☐ y ☐ n

Activities Accomplished:

☐ Archery
☐ Biking
☐ Birding
☐ Boating
☐ Camping
☐ Caving
☐ Geocaching

☐ Fishing
☐ Hiking
☐ Horseback Riding
☐ Hunting
☐ Off-Roading
☐ Paddle Boarding
☐ Photography

☐ Picknicking
☐ Rock Climbing
☐ Shooting Range
☐ Snowshoeing
☐ Stargazing
☐ Swimming
☐ Tennis

☐ Walking
☐ Wildlife Watching
☐ _____
☐ _____
☐ _____
☐ _____
☐ _____

Traveling by:

☐ ☐ ☐ ☐ ☐ ☐ ☐ ☐ ☐ ☐ ☐ ☐

Add your favorite ticket stub, postcard, photo, stamp or drawing here

LET NEW ADVENTURES
≫ BEGIN →

Carmel River State Beach

County: Monterey

Established: 1953   *Acres: 297*

Protects a 1-mile-long (1.6 km) beach and a lagoon at the mouth of the Carmel Riverwhich attracts many migratory birds.

Star Rating
☆ ☆ ☆ ☆ ☆

My favorite thing about this place is... _____

Why I went ... _____

Who I went with ... _____

When I went ... _____

What I did... _____

What I saw... _____

What I learned... _____

An unforgettable moment... _____

A laughable moment... _____

A surprising moment... _____

An unforeseeable moment... _____

Wildlife spotted... _____

List
- [ ] _____
- [ ] _____
- [ ] _____
- [ ] _____
- [ ] _____
- [ ] _____
- [ ] _____
- [ ] _____
- [ ] _____
- [ ] _____
- [ ] _____
- [ ] _____
- [ ] _____
- [ ] _____
- [ ] _____
- [ ] _____
- [ ] _____
- [ ] _____
- [ ] _____
- [ ] _____
- [ ] _____

Snapped a selfie | Location... _____

Took a park sign photo? - ☐ y ☐ n

The weather was ... ☐ ☐ ☐ ☐ ☐ ☐ ☐

PLAN YOUR TRIP:

☐ Day Trip   ☐ Overnight Stay

Reservations required: ☐ y ☐ n

Date reservations made: _____

Refund Policy: ☐ y ☐ n Site #: _____

Confirmation #: _____

Miles to travel: _____

Time traveling: _____

RV's?: ☐ y ☐ n Largest size RV? _____

Activities Accomplished:

☐ Archery
☐ Biking
☐ Birding
☐ Boating
☐ Camping
☐ Caving
☐ Geocaching

☐ Fishing
☐ Hiking
☐ Horseback Riding
☐ Hunting
☐ Off-Roading
☐ Paddle Boarding
☐ Photography

☐ Picknicking
☐ Rock Climbing
☐ Shooting Range
☐ Snowshoeing
☐ Stargazing
☐ Swimming
☐ Tennis

☐ Walking
☐ Wildlife Watching
☐ _____
☐ _____
☐ _____
☐ _____
☐ _____

RESERVATION INFORMATION:

Address: _____
_____

Reserved dates: _____

Check-in time: _____   Early check-in?: ☐ y ☐ n

Check-out time: _____   Late check-out?: ☐ y ☐ n

Website: _____

Phone: _____

WiFi: _____   WiFi password: _____

Dog friendly?: ☐ y ☐ n   Open all year?: ☐ y ☐ n

Traveling by:

☐ ☐ ☐ ☐ ☐ ☐ ☐ ☐ ☐ ☐ ☐ ☐

Add your favorite ticket stub, postcard, photo, stamp or drawing here

LET NEW ADVENTURES
»» BEGIN →

CARPINTERIA STATE BEACH

County: Santa Barbara and Ventura

Established: 1932

Acres: 62

Offers a mile-long beach in the city of Carpinteria.

Star Rating
☆ ☆ ☆ ☆ ☆

My favorite thing about this place is... _____

Why I went ... _____

Who I went with ... _____

When I went ... _____

What I did... _____

What I saw... _____

What I learned... _____

An unforgettable moment... _____

A laughable moment... _____

A surprising moment... _____

An unforeseeable moment... _____

Wildlife spotted... _____

List
- [ ] _____
- [ ] _____
- [ ] _____
- [ ] _____
- [ ] _____
- [ ] _____
- [ ] _____
- [ ] _____
- [ ] _____
- [ ] _____
- [ ] _____
- [ ] _____
- [ ] _____
- [ ] _____
- [ ] _____
- [ ] _____
- [ ] _____
- [ ] _____
- [ ] _____

📷 Snapped a selfie | Location...

📷 Took a park sign photo? - ☐ y ☐ n

The weather was ...
☐ ☐ ☐ ☐ ☐ ☐ ☐

PLAN YOUR TRIP:

☐ Day Trip   ☐ Overnight Stay

Reservations required: ☐ y ☐ n

Date reservations made: _____

Refund Policy: ☐ y ☐ n Site #: _____

Confirmation #: _____

Miles to travel: _____

Time traveling: _____

RV's?: ☐ y ☐ n Largest size RV? _____

Activities Accomplished:

☐ Archery
☐ Biking
☐ Birding
☐ Boating
☐ Camping
☐ Caving
☐ Geocaching

☐ Fishing
☐ Hiking
☐ Horseback Riding
☐ Hunting
☐ Off-Roading
☐ Paddle Boarding
☐ Photography

☐ Picknicking
☐ Rock Climbing
☐ Shooting Range
☐ Snowshoeing
☐ Stargazing
☐ Swimming
☐ Tennis

☐ Walking
☐ Wildlife Watching
☐ _____
☐ _____
☐ _____
☐ _____
☐ _____

RESERVATION INFORMATION:

Address: _____
_____

Reserved dates: _____

Check-in time: _____   Early check-in?: ☐ y ☐ n

Check-out time: _____   Late check-out?: ☐ y ☐ n

Website: _____

Phone: _____

WiFi: _____   WiFi password: _____

Dog friendly?: ☐ y ☐ n   Open all year?: ☐ y ☐ n

Traveling by:

☐ ☐ ☐ ☐ ☐ ☐ ☐ ☐ ☐ ☐ ☐ ☐

Add your favorite ticket stub, postcard, photo, stamp or drawing here

LET NEW ADVENTURES
≫ BEGIN →

Caspar Headlands State Beach

County: Mendocino

Established: 1972   *Acres:* 75

Star Rating

☆ ☆ ☆ ☆ ☆

My favorite thing about this place is... _____

Why I went ... _____

Who I went with ... _____

When I went ... _____

What I did... _____

What I saw... _____

What I learned... _____

An unforgettable moment... _____

A laughable moment... _____

A surprising moment... _____

An unforeseeable moment... _____

Wildlife spotted... _____

⊙ Snapped a selfie | Location... _____

⊙ Took a park sign photo? - ☐ y ☐ n

List

- ☐ _____
- ☐ _____
- ☐ _____
- ☐ _____
- ☐ _____
- ☐ _____
- ☐ _____
- ☐ _____
- ☐ _____
- ☐ _____
- ☐ _____
- ☐ _____
- ☐ _____
- ☐ _____
- ☐ _____
- ☐ _____
- ☐ _____
- ☐ _____

The weather was ...   ☐ ☐ ☐ ☐ ☐ ☐ ☐

PLAN YOUR TRIP:

☐ Day Trip   ☐ Overnight Stay

Reservations required: ☐ y ☐ n

Date reservations made: _____

Refund Policy: ☐ y ☐ n Site #: _____

Confirmation #: _____

Miles to travel: _____

Time traveling: _____

RV's?: ☐ y ☐ n Largest size RV? _____

Activities Accomplished:

☐ Archery
☐ Biking
☐ Birding
☐ Boating
☐ Camping
☐ Caving
☐ Geocaching

☐ Fishing
☐ Hiking
☐ Horseback Riding
☐ Hunting
☐ Off-Roading
☐ Paddle Boarding
☐ Photography

☐ Picknicking
☐ Rock Climbing
☐ Shooting Range
☐ Snowshoeing
☐ Stargazing
☐ Swimming
☐ Tennis

☐ Walking
☐ Wildlife Watching
☐ _____
☐ _____
☐ _____
☐ _____
☐ _____

RESERVATION INFORMATION:

Address: _____
_____

Reserved dates: _____

Check-in time: _____ Early check-in?: ☐ y ☐ n

Check-out time: _____ Late check-out?: ☐ y ☐ n

Website: _____

Phone: _____

WiFi: _____ WiFi password: _____

Dog friendly?: ☐ y ☐ n   Open all year?: ☐ y ☐ n

Traveling by:

☐ ☐ ☐ ☐ ☐ ☐ ☐ ☐ ☐ ☐ ☐ ☐

Add your favorite ticket stub, postcard, photo, stamp or drawing here

LET NEW ADVENTURES
≫ BEGIN →

CAYUCOS STATE BEACH

County: San Luis Obispo

Established: 1940

Acres: 16

Provides a swimming and surfing beach in the beach town of Cayucos.

Star Rating
☆ ☆ ☆ ☆ ☆

My favorite thing about this place is... _____

Why I went ... _____

Who I went with ... _____

When I went ... _____

What I did... _____

What I saw... _____

What I learned... _____

An unforgettable moment... _____

A laughable moment... _____

A surprising moment... _____

An unforeseeable moment... _____

Wildlife spotted... _____

List
- [ ] _____
- [ ] _____
- [ ] _____
- [ ] _____
- [ ] _____
- [ ] _____
- [ ] _____
- [ ] _____
- [ ] _____
- [ ] _____
- [ ] _____
- [ ] _____
- [ ] _____
- [ ] _____
- [ ] _____
- [ ] _____
- [ ] _____
- [ ] _____

📷 Snapped a selfie | Location...

📷 Took a park sign photo? - ☐ y ☐ n

The weather was ... ☐ ☐ ☐ ☐ ☐ ☐ ☐

PLAN YOUR TRIP:

☐ Day Trip   ☐ Overnight Stay

Reservations required: ☐ y ☐ n

Date reservations made: _____

Refund Policy: ☐ y ☐ n Site #: _____

Confirmation #: _____

Miles to travel: _____

Time traveling: _____

RV's?: ☐ y ☐ n Largest size RV? _____

Activities Accomplished:

☐ Archery
☐ Biking
☐ Birding
☐ Boating
☐ Camping
☐ Caving
☐ Geocaching

☐ Fishing
☐ Hiking
☐ Horseback Riding
☐ Hunting
☐ Off-Roading
☐ Paddle Boarding
☐ Photography

☐ Picknicking
☐ Rock Climbing
☐ Shooting Range
☐ Snowshoeing
☐ Stargazing
☐ Swimming
☐ Tennis

☐ Walking
☐ Wildlife Watching
☐ _____
☐ _____
☐ _____
☐ _____
☐ _____

RESERVATION INFORMATION:

Address: _____
_____

Reserved dates: _____

Check-in time: _____ Early check-in?: ☐ y ☐ n

Check-out time: _____ Late check-out?: ☐ y ☐ n

Website: _____

Phone: _____

WiFi: _____ WiFi password: _____

Dog friendly?: ☐ y ☐ n   Open all year?: ☐ y ☐ n

Traveling by:

☐ ☐ ☐ ☐ ☐ ☐ ☐ ☐ ☐ ☐ ☐ ☐

Add your favorite ticket stub, postcard, photo, stamp or drawing here

LET NEW ADVENTURES
»› BEGIN →

Corona del Mar State Beach

County: Orange

Established: 1947

Acres: 30

Provides a half-mile-long swimming beach adjacent to the Newport Beach harbor jetty.

Star Rating
☆☆☆☆☆

My favorite thing about this place is... _____

Why I went ... _____

Who I went with ... _____

When I went ... _____

What I did... _____

What I saw... _____

What I learned... _____

An unforgettable moment... _____

A laughable moment... _____

A surprising moment... _____

An unforeseeable moment... _____

Wildlife spotted... _____

Snapped a selfie | Location... _____

Took a park sign photo? - ☐ y ☐ n

The weather was ...

List
- ☐ _____
- ☐ _____
- ☐ _____
- ☐ _____
- ☐ _____
- ☐ _____
- ☐ _____
- ☐ _____
- ☐ _____
- ☐ _____
- ☐ _____
- ☐ _____
- ☐ _____
- ☐ _____
- ☐ _____
- ☐ _____
- ☐ _____
- ☐ _____
- ☐ _____

PLAN YOUR TRIP:

☐ Day Trip   ☐ Overnight Stay

Reservations required: ☐ y ☐ n

Date reservations made: _____

Refund Policy: ☐ y ☐ n   Site #: _____

Confirmation #: _____

Miles to travel: _____

Time traveling: _____

RV's?: ☐ y ☐ n Largest size RV? _____

Activities Accomplished:

☐ Archery
☐ Biking
☐ Birding
☐ Boating
☐ Camping
☐ Caving
☐ Geocaching

☐ Fishing
☐ Hiking
☐ Horseback Riding
☐ Hunting
☐ Off-Roading
☐ Paddle Boarding
☐ Photography

☐ Picknicking
☐ Rock Climbing
☐ Shooting Range
☐ Snowshoeing
☐ Stargazing
☐ Swimming
☐ Tennis

☐ Walking
☐ Wildlife Watching
☐ _____
☐ _____
☐ _____
☐ _____
☐ _____

Traveling by:

☐   ☐   ☐   ☐   ☐   ☐   ☐   ☐   ☐   ☐   ☐   ☐

RESERVATION INFORMATION:

Address: _____
_____

Reserved dates: _____

Check-in time: _____   Early check-in?: ☐ y ☐ n

Check-out time: _____   Late check-out?: ☐ y ☐ n

Website: _____

Phone: _____

WiFi: _____   WiFi password: _____

Dog friendly?: ☐ y ☐ n   Open all year?: ☐ y ☐ n

Add your favorite ticket stub, postcard, photo, stamp or drawing here

LET NEW ADVENTURES
≫ BEGIN →

DOCKWEILER STATE BEACH

County: Los Angeles

Established: 1948   *Acres: 91*

Features 3 miles (4.8 km) of beach and a hang gliding training site, adjacent to Los Angeles International Airport.

Star Rating

☆☆☆☆☆

My favorite thing about this place is... _____

Why I went ... _____

Who I went with ... _____

When I went ... _____

What I did... _____

What I saw... _____

What I learned... _____

An unforgettable moment... _____

A laughable moment... _____

A surprising moment... _____

An unforeseeable moment... _____

Wildlife spotted... _____

Snapped a selfie | Location... _____

Took a park sign photo? - ☐ y ☐ n

The weather was ...

List

- ☐ _____
- ☐ _____
- ☐ _____
- ☐ _____
- ☐ _____
- ☐ _____
- ☐ _____
- ☐ _____
- ☐ _____
- ☐ _____
- ☐ _____
- ☐ _____
- ☐ _____
- ☐ _____
- ☐ _____
- ☐ _____
- ☐ _____
- ☐ _____
- ☐ _____
- ☐ _____
- ☐ _____

PLAN YOUR TRIP:

☐ Day Trip   ☐ Overnight Stay

Reservations required: ☐y ☐n

Date reservations made: _____

Refund Policy: ☐y ☐n Site #: _____

Confirmation #: _____

Miles to travel: _____

Time traveling: _____

RV's?: ☐y ☐n Largest size RV? _____

Activities Accomplished:

☐ Archery
☐ Biking
☐ Birding
☐ Boating
☐ Camping
☐ Caving
☐ Geocaching

☐ Fishing
☐ Hiking
☐ Horseback Riding
☐ Hunting
☐ Off-Roading
☐ Paddle Boarding
☐ Photography

☐ Picknicking
☐ Rock Climbing
☐ Shooting Range
☐ Snowshoeing
☐ Stargazing
☐ Swimming
☐ Tennis

☐ Walking
☐ Wildlife Watching
☐ _____
☐ _____
☐ _____
☐ _____
☐ _____

Traveling by:

☐ ☐ ☐ ☐ ☐ ☐ ☐ ☐ ☐ ☐ ☐ ☐

RESERVATION INFORMATION:

Address: _____
_____

Reserved dates: _____

Check-in time: _____ Early check-in?: ☐y ☐n

Check-out time: _____ Late check-out?: ☐y ☐n

Website: _____

Phone: _____

WiFi: _____ WiFi password: _____

Dog friendly?: ☐y ☐n   Open all year?: ☐y ☐n

Add your favorite ticket stub, postcard, photo, stamp or drawing here

LET NEW ADVENTURES
≫ BEGIN →

DOHENY STATE BEACH

County: Orange

Established: 1931

Acres: 254

Offers surfing and beach-front camping in Dana Point.

Star Rating
☆ ☆ ☆ ☆ ☆

My favorite thing about this place is... _____

Why I went ... _____

Who I went with ... _____

When I went ... _____

What I did... _____

What I saw... _____

What I learned... _____

An unforgettable moment... _____

A laughable moment... _____

A surprising moment... _____

An unforeseeable moment... _____

Wildlife spotted... _____

Snapped a selfie | Location... _____

Took a park sign photo? - ☐ y ☐ n

List

- ☐ _____
- ☐ _____
- ☐ _____
- ☐ _____
- ☐ _____
- ☐ _____
- ☐ _____
- ☐ _____
- ☐ _____
- ☐ _____
- ☐ _____
- ☐ _____
- ☐ _____
- ☐ _____
- ☐ _____
- ☐ _____
- ☐ _____
- ☐ _____
- ☐ _____

The weather was ... ☐ ☐ ☐ ☐ ☐ ☐ ☐

PLAN YOUR TRIP:

☐ Day Trip   ☐ Overnight Stay

Reservations required: ☐ y ☐ n

Date reservations made: _____

Refund Policy: ☐ y ☐ n Site #: _____

Confirmation #: _____

Miles to travel: _____

Time traveling: _____

RV's?: ☐ y ☐ n Largest size RV? _____

Activities Accomplished:

☐ Archery
☐ Biking
☐ Birding
☐ Boating
☐ Camping
☐ Caving
☐ Geocaching

☐ Fishing
☐ Hiking
☐ Horseback Riding
☐ Hunting
☐ Off-Roading
☐ Paddle Boarding
☐ Photography

☐ Picknicking
☐ Rock Climbing
☐ Shooting Range
☐ Snowshoeing
☐ Stargazing
☐ Swimming
☐ Tennis

☐ Walking
☐ Wildlife Watching
☐ _____
☐ _____
☐ _____
☐ _____
☐ _____

RESERVATION INFORMATION:

Address: _____
_____

Reserved dates: _____

Check-in time: _____ Early check-in?: ☐ y ☐ n

Check-out time: _____ Late check-out?: ☐ y ☐ n

Website: _____

Phone: _____

WiFi: _____ WiFi password: _____

Dog friendly?: ☐ y ☐ n   Open all year?: ☐ y ☐ n

Traveling by:

☐ ☐ ☐ ☐ ☐ ☐ ☐ ☐ ☐ ☐ ☐ ☐

Add your favorite ticket stub, postcard, photo, stamp or drawing here

LET NEW ADVENTURES
≫ BEGIN →

EL CAPITⱯ°N STATE BEACH

County: Santa Barbara

Established: 1953

Acres: 2,634

Features a narrow beach at the foot of coastal bluffs where monarch butterflies congregate in autumn.

Star Rating
☆ ☆ ☆ ☆ ☆

My favorite thing about this place is...

Why I went ...

Who I went with ...

When I went ...

What I did...

What I saw...

What I learned...

An unforgettable moment...

A laughable moment...

A surprising moment...

An unforeseeable moment...

Wildlife spotted...

List

- ☐
- ☐
- ☐
- ☐
- ☐
- ☐
- ☐
- ☐
- ☐
- ☐
- ☐
- ☐
- ☐
- ☐
- ☐
- ☐
- ☐
- ☐
- ☐
- ☐

Snapped a selfie | Location...

Took a park sign photo? - ☐ y ☐ n

The weather was ...
☐ ☐ ☐ ☐ ☐ ☐ ☐

PLAN YOUR TRIP:

☐ Day Trip   ☐ Overnight Stay

Reservations required: ☐ y ☐ n

Date reservations made: _____

Refund Policy: ☐ y ☐ n Site #: _____

Confirmation #: _____

Miles to travel: _____

Time traveling: _____

RV's?: ☐ y ☐ n Largest size RV? _____

Activities Accomplished:

☐ Archery
☐ Biking
☐ Birding
☐ Boating
☐ Camping
☐ Caving
☐ Geocaching

☐ Fishing
☐ Hiking
☐ Horseback Riding
☐ Hunting
☐ Off-Roading
☐ Paddle Boarding
☐ Photography

☐ Picknicking
☐ Rock Climbing
☐ Shooting Range
☐ Snowshoeing
☐ Stargazing
☐ Swimming
☐ Tennis

☐ Walking
☐ Wildlife Watching
☐ _____
☐ _____
☐ _____
☐ _____
☐ _____

RESERVATION INFORMATION:

Address: _____
_____

Reserved dates: _____

Check-in time: _____ Early check-in?: ☐ y ☐ n

Check-out time: _____ Late check-out?: ☐ y ☐ n

Website: _____

Phone: _____

WiFi: _____ WiFi password: _____

Dog friendly?: ☐ y ☐ n   Open all year?: ☐ y ☐ n

Traveling by:

☐ ☐ ☐ ☐ ☐ ☐ ☐ ☐ ☐ ☐ ☐ ☐

Add your favorite ticket stub, postcard, photo, stamp or drawing here

LET NEW ADVENTURES
»» BEGIN →

EMMA WOOD STATE BEACH

County: Ventura

Established: 1957

Acres: 112

Contains a surfing beach and an estuary at the mouth of the Ventura River.

Star Rating
☆ ☆ ☆ ☆ ☆

My favorite thing about this place is... _____

Why I went ... _____

Who I went with ... _____

When I went ... _____

What I did... _____

What I saw... _____

What I learned... _____

An unforgettable moment... _____

A laughable moment... _____

A surprising moment... _____

An unforeseeable moment... _____

Wildlife spotted... _____

List
- [ ] _____
- [ ] _____
- [ ] _____
- [ ] _____
- [ ] _____
- [ ] _____
- [ ] _____
- [ ] _____
- [ ] _____
- [ ] _____
- [ ] _____
- [ ] _____
- [ ] _____
- [ ] _____
- [ ] _____
- [ ] _____
- [ ] _____

Snapped a selfie | Location...

Took a park sign photo? - ☐ y ☐ n

The weather was ...

PLAN YOUR TRIP:

☐ Day Trip   ☐ Overnight Stay

Reservations required: ☐ y ☐ n

Date reservations made: _____

Refund Policy: ☐ y ☐ n Site #: _____

Confirmation #: _____

Miles to travel: _____

Time traveling: _____

RV's?: ☐ y ☐ n Largest size RV? _____

Activities Accomplished:

☐ Archery
☐ Biking
☐ Birding
☐ Boating
☐ Camping
☐ Caving
☐ Geocaching

☐ Fishing
☐ Hiking
☐ Horseback Riding
☐ Hunting
☐ Off-Roading
☐ Paddle Boarding
☐ Photography

☐ Picknicking
☐ Rock Climbing
☐ Shooting Range
☐ Snowshoeing
☐ Stargazing
☐ Swimming
☐ Tennis

☐ Walking
☐ Wildlife Watching
☐ _____
☐ _____
☐ _____
☐ _____
☐ _____

RESERVATION INFORMATION:

Address: _____
_____

Reserved dates: _____

Check-in time: _____   Early check-in?: ☐ y ☐ n

Check-out time: _____   Late check-out?: ☐ y ☐ n

Website: _____

Phone: _____

WiFi: _____   WiFi password: _____

Dog friendly?: ☐ y ☐ n   Open all year?: ☐ y ☐ n

Traveling by:

☐ ☐ ☐ ☐ ☐ ☐ ☐ ☐ ☐ ☐ ☐ ☐

Add your favorite ticket stub, postcard, photo, stamp or drawing here

LET NEW ADVENTURES
≫ BEGIN →

GRAY WHALE COVE STATE BEACH

County: San Mateo

Established: 1966   Acres: 3.1

Embraces a steep-walled cove, near the Devil's Slide, where gray whales are often seen close to shore.

Star Rating
☆ ☆ ☆ ☆ ☆

My favorite thing about this place is... _____

Why I went ... _____

Who I went with ... _____

When I went ... _____

What I did... _____

What I saw... _____

What I learned... _____

An unforgettable moment... _____

A laughable moment... _____

A surprising moment... _____

An unforeseeable moment... _____

Wildlife spotted... _____

List

- ☐ _____
- ☐ _____
- ☐ _____
- ☐ _____
- ☐ _____
- ☐ _____
- ☐ _____
- ☐ _____
- ☐ _____
- ☐ _____
- ☐ _____
- ☐ _____
- ☐ _____
- ☐ _____
- ☐ _____
- ☐ _____
- ☐ _____
- ☐ _____
- ☐ _____

Snapped a selfie | Location... _____

Took a park sign photo? - ☐ y ☐ n

The weather was ...
☐   ☐   ☐   ☐   ☐   ☐   ☐

PLAN YOUR TRIP:

☐ Day Trip   ☐ Overnight Stay

Reservations required: ☐ y ☐ n

Date reservations made: _____

Refund Policy: ☐ y ☐ n Site #: _____

Confirmation #: _____

Miles to travel: _____

Time traveling: _____

RV's?: ☐ y ☐ n Largest size RV? _____

Activities Accomplished:

☐ Archery
☐ Biking
☐ Birding
☐ Boating
☐ Camping
☐ Caving
☐ Geocaching

☐ Fishing
☐ Hiking
☐ Horseback Riding
☐ Hunting
☐ Off-Roading
☐ Paddle Boarding
☐ Photography

☐ Picknicking
☐ Rock Climbing
☐ Shooting Range
☐ Snowshoeing
☐ Stargazing
☐ Swimming
☐ Tennis

☐ Walking
☐ Wildlife Watching
☐ _____
☐ _____
☐ _____
☐ _____
☐ _____

Traveling by:

☐ ☐ ☐ ☐ ☐ ☐ ☐ ☐ ☐ ☐ ☐ ☐

RESERVATION INFORMATION:

Address: _____
_____

Reserved dates: _____

Check-in time: _____   Early check-in?: ☐ y ☐ n

Check-out time: _____   Late check-out?: ☐ y ☐ n

Website: _____

Phone: _____

WiFi: _____   WiFi password: _____

Dog friendly?: ☐ y ☐ n   Open all year?: ☐ y ☐ n

Add your favorite ticket stub, postcard, photo, stamp or drawing here

LET NEW ADVENTURES
»» BEGIN →

Greenwood State Beach

County: Mendocino

Established: 1978   *Acres: 47*

Features a picturesque beach in Elk and a visitor center interpreting the town's lumbering history.

Star Rating
☆ ☆ ☆ ☆ ☆

My favorite thing about this place is... _____

Why I went ... _____

Who I went with ... _____

When I went ... _____

What I did... _____

What I saw... _____

What I learned... _____

An unforgettable moment... _____

A laughable moment... _____

A surprising moment... _____

An unforeseeable moment... _____

Wildlife spotted... _____

List
- [ ] _____
- [ ] _____
- [ ] _____
- [ ] _____
- [ ] _____
- [ ] _____
- [ ] _____
- [ ] _____
- [ ] _____
- [ ] _____
- [ ] _____
- [ ] _____
- [ ] _____
- [ ] _____
- [ ] _____
- [ ] _____
- [ ] _____

📷 Snapped a selfie | Location... _____

📷 Took a park sign photo? - ☐ y ☐ n

The weather was ...
☐ ☐ ☐ ☐ ☐ ☐ ☐

PLAN YOUR TRIP:

☐ Day Trip　　　　☐ Overnight Stay

Reservations required: ☐ y ☐ n

Date reservations made: _____

Refund Policy: ☐ y ☐ n　Site #: _____

Confirmation #: _____

Miles to travel: _____

Time traveling: _____

RV's?: ☐ y ☐ n Largest size RV? _____

Activities Accomplished:

☐ Archery	☐ Fishing	☐ Picknicking	☐ Walking
☐ Biking	☐ Hiking	☐ Rock Climbing	☐ Wildlife Watching
☐ Birding	☐ Horseback Riding	☐ Shooting Range	☐ _____
☐ Boating	☐ Hunting	☐ Snowshoeing	☐ _____
☐ Camping	☐ Off-Roading	☐ Stargazing	☐ _____
☐ Caving	☐ Paddle Boarding	☐ Swimming	☐ _____
☐ Geocaching	☐ Photography	☐ Tennis	☐ _____

Traveling by:

☐　☐　☐　☐　☐　☐　☐　☐　☐　☐　☐　☐

RESERVATION INFORMATION:

Address: _____
_____

Reserved dates: _____

Check-in time: _____　Early check-in?: ☐ y ☐ n

Check-out time: _____　Late check-out?: ☐ y ☐ n

Website: _____

Phone: _____

WiFi: _____　WiFi password: _____

Dog friendly?: ☐ y ☐ n　Open all year?: ☐ y ☐ n

Add your favorite ticket stub, postcard, photo, stamp or drawing here

LET NEW ADVENTURES
≫ BEGIN →

Half Moon Bay State Beach

County: San Mateo

Established: 1956

Acres: 181

Encompasses four popular sandy beaches on Half Moon Bay.

Star Rating
☆ ☆ ☆ ☆ ☆

My favorite thing about this place is... _____

Why I went ... _____

Who I went with ... _____

When I went ... _____

What I did... _____

What I saw... _____

What I learned... _____

An unforgettable moment... _____

A laughable moment... _____

A surprising moment... _____

An unforeseeable moment... _____

Wildlife spotted... _____

List

- ☐ _____
- ☐ _____
- ☐ _____
- ☐ _____
- ☐ _____
- ☐ _____
- ☐ _____
- ☐ _____
- ☐ _____
- ☐ _____
- ☐ _____
- ☐ _____
- ☐ _____
- ☐ _____
- ☐ _____
- ☐ _____
- ☐ _____
- ☐ _____

Snapped a selfie | Location... _____

Took a park sign photo? - ☐ y ☐ n

The weather was ...
☐ ☐ ☐ ☐ ☐ ☐ ☐

PLAN YOUR TRIP:

☐ Day Trip   ☐ Overnight Stay

Reservations required: ☐ y ☐ n

Date reservations made: _____

Refund Policy: ☐ y ☐ n Site #: _____

Confirmation #: _____

Miles to travel: _____

Time traveling: _____

RV's?: ☐ y ☐ n Largest size RV? _____

Activities Accomplished:

☐ Archery	☐ Fishing	☐ Picknicking	☐ Walking
☐ Biking	☐ Hiking	☐ Rock Climbing	☐ Wildlife Watching
☐ Birding	☐ Horseback Riding	☐ Shooting Range	☐ _____
☐ Boating	☐ Hunting	☐ Snowshoeing	☐ _____
☐ Camping	☐ Off-Roading	☐ Stargazing	☐ _____
☐ Caving	☐ Paddle Boarding	☐ Swimming	☐ _____
☐ Geocaching	☐ Photography	☐ Tennis	☐ _____

Traveling by:

☐ ☐ ☐ ☐ ☐ ☐ ☐ ☐ ☐ ☐ ☐ ☐

RESERVATION INFORMATION:

Address: _____
_____

Reserved dates: _____

Check-in time: _____ Early check-in?: ☐ y ☐ n

Check-out time: _____ Late check-out?: ☐ y ☐ n

Website: _____

Phone: _____

WiFi: _____ WiFi password: _____

Dog friendly?: ☐ y ☐ n   Open all year?: ☐ y ☐ n

Add your favorite ticket stub, postcard, photo, stamp or drawing here

LET NEW ADVENTURES
≫ BEGIN →

Huntington State Beach

County: Orange

Established: 1942

Acres: 121

Contains 2 miles (3.2 km) of wide, flat beach in the city of Huntington Beach.

Star Rating
☆ ☆ ☆ ☆ ☆

My favorite thing about this place is...

Why I went ...

Who I went with ...

When I went ...

What I did...

What I saw...

What I learned...

An unforgettable moment...

List
- ☐
- ☐
- ☐
- ☐
- ☐
- ☐
- ☐
- ☐
- ☐
- ☐
- ☐
- ☐
- ☐
- ☐
- ☐
- ☐
- ☐
- ☐
- ☐
- ☐
- ☐

A laughable moment...

A surprising moment...

An unforeseeable moment...

Wildlife spotted...

Snapped a selfie | Location...

Took a park sign photo? - ☐ y ☐ n

The weather was ...
☐ ☐ ☐ ☐ ☐ ☐ ☐

PLAN YOUR TRIP:

☐ Day Trip   ☐ Overnight Stay

Reservations required: ☐ y ☐ n

Date reservations made: _____

Refund Policy: ☐ y ☐ n Site #: _____

Confirmation #: _____

Miles to travel: _____

Time traveling: _____

RV's?: ☐ y ☐ n Largest size RV? _____

Activities Accomplished:

☐ Archery
☐ Biking
☐ Birding
☐ Boating
☐ Camping
☐ Caving
☐ Geocaching

☐ Fishing
☐ Hiking
☐ Horseback Riding
☐ Hunting
☐ Off-Roading
☐ Paddle Boarding
☐ Photography

☐ Picknicking
☐ Rock Climbing
☐ Shooting Range
☐ Snowshoeing
☐ Stargazing
☐ Swimming
☐ Tennis

☐ Walking
☐ Wildlife Watching
☐ _____
☐ _____
☐ _____
☐ _____
☐ _____

RESERVATION INFORMATION:

Address: _____
_____

Reserved dates: _____

Check-in time: _____ Early check-in?: ☐ y ☐ n

Check-out time: _____ Late check-out?: ☐ y ☐ n

Website: _____

Phone: _____

WiFi: _____ WiFi password: _____

Dog friendly?: ☐ y ☐ n   Open all year?: ☐ y ☐ n

Traveling by:

☐ ☐ ☐ ☐ ☐ ☐ ☐ ☐ ☐ ☐ ☐ ☐

Add your favorite ticket stub, postcard, photo, stamp or drawing here

LET NEW ADVENTURES
»» BEGIN →

Leucadia State Beach

County: San Diego

Established: 1949

Acres: 10.6

Comprises a small, rocky beach in Encinitas.

Star Rating

☆ ☆ ☆ ☆ ☆

My favorite thing about this place is...

Why I went ...

Who I went with ...

When I went ...

What I did...

What I saw...

What I learned...

An unforgettable moment...

A laughable moment...

A surprising moment...

An unforeseeable moment...

Wildlife spotted...

List

☐
☐
☐
☐
☐
☐
☐
☐
☐
☐
☐
☐
☐
☐
☐
☐
☐
☐

Snapped a selfie | Location...

Took a park sign photo? - ☐ y ☐ n

The weather was ...

☐ ☐ ☐ ☐ ☐ ☐ ☐

PLAN YOUR TRIP:

☐ Day Trip   ☐ Overnight Stay

Reservations required: ☐ y ☐ n

Date reservations made: _____

Refund Policy: ☐ y ☐ n Site #: _____

Confirmation #: _____

Miles to travel: _____

Time traveling: _____

RV's?: ☐ y ☐ n Largest size RV? _____

RESERVATION INFORMATION:

Address: _____

_____

Reserved dates: _____

Check-in time: _____ Early check-in?: ☐ y ☐ n

Check-out time: _____ Late check-out?: ☐ y ☐ n

Website: _____

Phone: _____

WiFi: _____ WiFi password: _____

Dog friendly?: ☐ y ☐ n   Open all year?: ☐ y ☐ n

Activities Accomplished:

☐ Archery
☐ Biking
☐ Birding
☐ Boating
☐ Camping
☐ Caving
☐ Geocaching

☐ Fishing
☐ Hiking
☐ Horseback Riding
☐ Hunting
☐ Off-Roading
☐ Paddle Boarding
☐ Photography

☐ Picknicking
☐ Rock Climbing
☐ Shooting Range
☐ Snowshoeing
☐ Stargazing
☐ Swimming
☐ Tennis

☐ Walking
☐ Wildlife Watching
☐ _____
☐ _____
☐ _____
☐ _____
☐ _____

Traveling by:

☐ ☐ ☐ ☐ ☐ ☐ ☐ ☐ ☐ ☐ ☐ ☐

Add your favorite ticket stub, postcard, photo, stamp or drawing here

LET NEW ADVENTURES
»» BEGIN →

LIGHTHOUSE FIELD STATE BEACH

County: Santa Cruz

Established: 1978

Acres: 38

Features the Steamer Lane surf break and a lighthouse containing the Santa Cruz Surfing Museum.

Star Rating
☆ ☆ ☆ ☆ ☆

My favorite thing about this place is... _____

Why I went ... _____

Who I went with ... _____

When I went ... _____

What I did... _____

What I saw... _____

What I learned... _____

An unforgettable moment... _____

A laughable moment... _____

A surprising moment... _____

An unforeseeable moment... _____

Wildlife spotted... _____

Snapped a selfie | Location... _____

Took a park sign photo? - ☐ y ☐ n

List
- ☐ _____
- ☐ _____
- ☐ _____
- ☐ _____
- ☐ _____
- ☐ _____
- ☐ _____
- ☐ _____
- ☐ _____
- ☐ _____
- ☐ _____
- ☐ _____
- ☐ _____
- ☐ _____
- ☐ _____
- ☐ _____
- ☐ _____
- ☐ _____
- ☐ _____

The weather was ...
☐ ☐ ☐ ☐ ☐ ☐ ☐

PLAN YOUR TRIP:

☐ Day Trip   ☐ Overnight Stay

Reservations required: ☐ y ☐ n

Date reservations made: _____

Refund Policy: ☐ y ☐ n Site #: _____

Confirmation #: _____

Miles to travel: _____

Time traveling: _____

RV's?: ☐ y ☐ n Largest size RV? _____

Activities Accomplished:

☐ Archery
☐ Biking
☐ Birding
☐ Boating
☐ Camping
☐ Caving
☐ Geocaching

☐ Fishing
☐ Hiking
☐ Horseback Riding
☐ Hunting
☐ Off-Roading
☐ Paddle Boarding
☐ Photography

☐ Picknicking
☐ Rock Climbing
☐ Shooting Range
☐ Snowshoeing
☐ Stargazing
☐ Swimming
☐ Tennis

☐ Walking
☐ Wildlife Watching
☐ _____
☐ _____
☐ _____
☐ _____
☐ _____

Traveling by:

☐ ☐ ☐ ☐ ☐ ☐ ☐ ☐ ☐ ☐ ☐ ☐

RESERVATION INFORMATION:

Address: _____
_____

Reserved dates: _____

Check-in time: _____   Early check-in?: ☐ y ☐ n

Check-out time: _____   Late check-out?: ☐ y ☐ n

Website: _____

Phone: _____

WiFi: _____   WiFi password: _____

Dog friendly?: ☐ y ☐ n   Open all year?: ☐ y ☐ n

Add your favorite ticket stub, postcard, photo, stamp or drawing here

LET NEW ADVENTURES
»» BEGIN →

LITTLE RIVER STATE BEACH

County: Humboldt

Established: 1931

Acres: 152

Comprises a broad open beach with dunes.

Star Rating
☆ ☆ ☆ ☆ ☆

My favorite thing about this place is... _____

Why I went ... _____

Who I went with ... _____

When I went ... _____

What I did... _____

What I saw... _____

What I learned... _____

An unforgettable moment... _____

A laughable moment... _____

A surprising moment... _____

An unforeseeable moment... _____

Wildlife spotted... _____

List
- [ ] _____
- [ ] _____
- [ ] _____
- [ ] _____
- [ ] _____
- [ ] _____
- [ ] _____
- [ ] _____
- [ ] _____
- [ ] _____
- [ ] _____
- [ ] _____
- [ ] _____
- [ ] _____
- [ ] _____
- [ ] _____
- [ ] _____
- [ ] _____
- [ ] _____

Snapped a selfie | Location... _____

Took a park sign photo? - ☐ y ☐ n

The weather was ...
☐ ☐ ☐ ☐ ☐ ☐ ☐

PLAN YOUR TRIP:

☐ Day Trip   ☐ Overnight Stay

Reservations required: ☐ y ☐ n

Date reservations made: _____

Refund Policy: ☐ y ☐ n Site #: _____

Confirmation #: _____

Miles to travel: _____

Time traveling: _____

RV's?: ☐ y ☐ n Largest size RV? _____

Activities Accomplished:

RESERVATION INFORMATION:

Address: _____
_____

Reserved dates: _____

Check-in time: _____ Early check-in?: ☐ y ☐ n

Check-out time: _____ Late check-out?: ☐ y ☐ n

Website: _____

Phone: _____

WiFi: _____ WiFi password: _____

Dog friendly?: ☐ y ☐ n   Open all year?: ☐ y ☐ n

☐ Archery
☐ Biking
☐ Birding
☐ Boating
☐ Camping
☐ Caving
☐ Geocaching

☐ Fishing
☐ Hiking
☐ Horseback Riding
☐ Hunting
☐ Off-Roading
☐ Paddle Boarding
☐ Photography

☐ Picknicking
☐ Rock Climbing
☐ Shooting Range
☐ Snowshoeing
☐ Stargazing
☐ Swimming
☐ Tennis

☐ Walking
☐ Wildlife Watching
☐ _____
☐ _____
☐ _____
☐ _____
☐ _____

Traveling by:

☐ ☐ ☐ ☐ ☐ ☐ ☐ ☐ ☐ ☐ ☐ ☐

Add your favorite ticket stub, postcard, photo, stamp or drawing here

LET NEW ADVENTURES
»» BEGIN →

Malibu Lagoon State Beach

County: Los Angeles

Established: 1951

Acres: 110

Star Rating

☆ ☆ ☆ ☆ ☆

My favorite thing about this place is... _____

Why I went ... _____

Who I went with ... _____

When I went ... _____

What I did... _____

What I saw... _____

What I learned... _____

An unforgettable moment... _____

A laughable moment... _____

A surprising moment... _____

An unforeseeable moment... _____

Wildlife spotted... _____

List

- ☐ _____
- ☐ _____
- ☐ _____
- ☐ _____
- ☐ _____
- ☐ _____
- ☐ _____
- ☐ _____
- ☐ _____
- ☐ _____
- ☐ _____
- ☐ _____
- ☐ _____
- ☐ _____
- ☐ _____
- ☐ _____
- ☐ _____
- ☐ _____

Snapped a selfie | Location...

Took a park sign photo? - ☐ y ☐ n

The weather was ...

☐ ☐ ☐ ☐ ☐ ☐ ☐

PLAN YOUR TRIP:

☐ Day Trip   ☐ Overnight Stay

Reservations required: ☐ y ☐ n

Date reservations made: _____

Refund Policy: ☐ y ☐ n   Site #: _____

Confirmation #: _____

Miles to travel: _____

Time traveling: _____

RV's?: ☐ y ☐ n Largest size RV? _____

Activities Accomplished:

☐ Archery
☐ Biking
☐ Birding
☐ Boating
☐ Camping
☐ Caving
☐ Geocaching

☐ Fishing
☐ Hiking
☐ Horseback Riding
☐ Hunting
☐ Off-Roading
☐ Paddle Boarding
☐ Photography

☐ Picknicking
☐ Rock Climbing
☐ Shooting Range
☐ Snowshoeing
☐ Stargazing
☐ Swimming
☐ Tennis

☐ Walking
☐ Wildlife Watching
☐ _____
☐ _____
☐ _____
☐ _____
☐ _____

RESERVATION INFORMATION:

Address: _____
_____

Reserved dates: _____

Check-in time: _____   Early check-in?: ☐ y ☐ n

Check-out time: _____   Late check-out?: ☐ y ☐ n

Website: _____

Phone: _____

WiFi: _____   WiFi password: _____

Dog friendly?: ☐ y ☐ n   Open all year?: ☐ y ☐ n

Traveling by:

☐ ☐ ☐ ☐ ☐ ☐ ☐ ☐ ☐ ☐ ☐ ☐

Add your favorite ticket stub, postcard, photo, stamp or drawing here

LET NEW ADVENTURES
≫ BEGIN →

Mandalay State Beach

County: Ventura

Established: 1985   *Acres: 92*

Star Rating
☆ ☆ ☆ ☆ ☆

My favorite thing about this place is... _____

Why I went ... _____

Who I went with ... _____

When I went ... _____

What I did... _____

What I saw... _____

What I learned... _____

An unforgettable moment... _____

A laughable moment... _____

A surprising moment... _____

An unforeseeable moment... _____

Wildlife spotted... _____

📷 Snapped a selfie | Location... _____

📷 Took a park sign photo? - ☐ y ☐ n

List
- ☐ _____
- ☐ _____
- ☐ _____
- ☐ _____
- ☐ _____
- ☐ _____
- ☐ _____
- ☐ _____
- ☐ _____
- ☐ _____
- ☐ _____
- ☐ _____
- ☐ _____
- ☐ _____
- ☐ _____
- ☐ _____
- ☐ _____
- ☐ _____

The weather was ... ☐ ☐ ☐ ☐ ☐ ☐ ☐

PLAN YOUR TRIP:

☐ Day Trip   ☐ Overnight Stay

Reservations required: ☐y ☐n

Date reservations made: _____

Refund Policy: ☐y ☐n Site #: _____

Confirmation #: _____

Miles to travel: _____

Time traveling: _____

RV's?: ☐y ☐n Largest size RV? _____

Activities Accomplished:

☐ Archery
☐ Biking
☐ Birding
☐ Boating
☐ Camping
☐ Caving
☐ Geocaching

☐ Fishing
☐ Hiking
☐ Horseback Riding
☐ Hunting
☐ Off-Roading
☐ Paddle Boarding
☐ Photography

☐ Picknicking
☐ Rock Climbing
☐ Shooting Range
☐ Snowshoeing
☐ Stargazing
☐ Swimming
☐ Tennis

☐ Walking
☐ Wildlife Watching
☐ _____
☐ _____
☐ _____
☐ _____
☐ _____

RESERVATION INFORMATION:

Address: _____
_____

Reserved dates: _____

Check-in time: _____ Early check-in?: ☐y ☐n

Check-out time: _____ Late check-out?: ☐y ☐n

Website: _____

Phone: _____

WiFi: _____ WiFi password: _____

Dog friendly?: ☐y ☐n   Open all year?: ☐y ☐n

Traveling by:

☐ ☐ ☐ ☐ ☐ ☐ ☐ ☐ ☐ ☐ ☐ ☐

Add your favorite ticket stub, postcard, photo, stamp or drawing here

LET NEW ADVENTURES
≫ BEGIN →

Manresa State Beach

County: Santa Cruz

Established: 1948   *Acres: 138*

Star Rating
☆ ☆ ☆ ☆ ☆

My favorite thing about this place is...

Why I went ...

Who I went with ...

When I went ...

What I did...

What I saw...

What I learned...

List

An unforgettable moment...

A laughable moment...

A surprising moment...

An unforeseeable moment...

Wildlife spotted...

Snapped a selfie | Location...

Took a park sign photo? - ☐ y ☐ n

The weather was ...

PLAN YOUR TRIP:

☐ Day Trip   ☐ Overnight Stay

Reservations required: ☐ y ☐ n

Date reservations made: _____

Refund Policy: ☐ y ☐ n Site #: _____

Confirmation #: _____

Miles to travel: _____

Time traveling: _____

RV's?: ☐ y ☐ n Largest size RV? _____

Activities Accomplished:

RESERVATION INFORMATION:

Address: _____
_____

Reserved dates: _____

Check-in time: _____ Early check-in?: ☐ y ☐ n

Check-out time: _____ Late check-out?: ☐ y ☐ n

Website: _____

Phone: _____

WiFi: _____ WiFi password: _____

Dog friendly?: ☐ y ☐ n   Open all year?: ☐ y ☐ n

☐ Archery	☐ Fishing	☐ Picknicking	☐ Walking
☐ Biking	☐ Hiking	☐ Rock Climbing	☐ Wildlife Watching
☐ Birding	☐ Horseback Riding	☐ Shooting Range	☐ _____
☐ Boating	☐ Hunting	☐ Snowshoeing	☐ _____
☐ Camping	☐ Off-Roading	☐ Stargazing	☐ _____
☐ Caving	☐ Paddle Boarding	☐ Swimming	☐ _____
☐ Geocaching	☐ Photography	☐ Tennis	☐ _____

Traveling by:

☐ ☐ ☐ ☐ ☐ ☐ ☐ ☐ ☐ ☐ ☐ ☐

Add your favorite ticket stub, postcard, photo, stamp or drawing here

LET NEW ADVENTURES
»» BEGIN →

Marina State Beach

County: Monterey

Established: 1977

Acres: 171

Star Rating
☆ ☆ ☆ ☆ ☆

My favorite thing about this place is...

Why I went ...

Who I went with ...

When I went ...

What I did...

What I saw...

What I learned...

An unforgettable moment...

A laughable moment...

A surprising moment...

An unforeseeable moment...

Wildlife spotted...

Snapped a selfie | Location...

Took a park sign photo? - ☐ y ☐ n

List
- ☐
- ☐
- ☐
- ☐
- ☐
- ☐
- ☐
- ☐
- ☐
- ☐
- ☐
- ☐
- ☐
- ☐
- ☐
- ☐
- ☐
- ☐
- ☐

The weather was ...
☐ ☐ ☐ ☐ ☐ ☐ ☐

PLAN YOUR TRIP:

☐ Day Trip   ☐ Overnight Stay

Reservations required: ☐ y ☐ n

Date reservations made: _____

Refund Policy: ☐ y ☐ n   Site #: _____

Confirmation #: _____

Miles to travel: _____

Time traveling: _____

RV's?: ☐ y ☐ n   Largest size RV? _____

Activities Accomplished:

☐ Archery
☐ Biking
☐ Birding
☐ Boating
☐ Camping
☐ Caving
☐ Geocaching

☐ Fishing
☐ Hiking
☐ Horseback Riding
☐ Hunting
☐ Off-Roading
☐ Paddle Boarding
☐ Photography

☐ Picknicking
☐ Rock Climbing
☐ Shooting Range
☐ Snowshoeing
☐ Stargazing
☐ Swimming
☐ Tennis

☐ Walking
☐ Wildlife Watching
☐ _____
☐ _____
☐ _____
☐ _____
☐ _____

Traveling by:

☐ ☐ ☐ ☐ ☐ ☐ ☐ ☐ ☐ ☐ ☐ ☐

RESERVATION INFORMATION:

Address: _____
_____

Reserved dates: _____

Check-in time: _____   Early check-in?: ☐ y ☐ n

Check-out time: _____   Late check-out?: ☐ y ☐ n

Website: _____

Phone: _____

WiFi: _____   WiFi password: _____

Dog friendly?: ☐ y ☐ n   Open all year?: ☐ y ☐ n

Add your favorite ticket stub, postcard, photo, stamp or drawing here

LET NEW ADVENTURES
≫ BEGIN →

McGrath State Beach

County: Ventura

Established: 1948

Acres: 314

Star Rating
☆☆☆☆☆

My favorite thing about this place is... _____

Why I went ... _____

Who I went with ... _____

When I went ... _____

What I did... _____

What I saw... _____

What I learned... _____

An unforgettable moment... _____

A laughable moment... _____

A surprising moment... _____

An unforeseeable moment... _____

Wildlife spotted... _____

Snapped a selfie | Location... _____

Took a park sign photo? - ☐ y ☐ n

The weather was ... ☐ ☐ ☐ ☐ ☐ ☐ ☐

List
- ☐ _____
- ☐ _____
- ☐ _____
- ☐ _____
- ☐ _____
- ☐ _____
- ☐ _____
- ☐ _____
- ☐ _____
- ☐ _____
- ☐ _____
- ☐ _____
- ☐ _____
- ☐ _____
- ☐ _____
- ☐ _____
- ☐ _____
- ☐ _____

PLAN YOUR TRIP:

☐ Day Trip   ☐ Overnight Stay

Reservations required: ☐ y ☐ n

Date reservations made: _____

Refund Policy: ☐ y ☐ n Site #: _____

Confirmation #: _____

Miles to travel: _____

Time traveling: _____

RV's?: ☐ y ☐ n Largest size RV? _____

Activities Accomplished:

☐ Archery
☐ Biking
☐ Birding
☐ Boating
☐ Camping
☐ Caving
☐ Geocaching

☐ Fishing
☐ Hiking
☐ Horseback Riding
☐ Hunting
☐ Off-Roading
☐ Paddle Boarding
☐ Photography

☐ Picknicking
☐ Rock Climbing
☐ Shooting Range
☐ Snowshoeing
☐ Stargazing
☐ Swimming
☐ Tennis

☐ Walking
☐ Wildlife Watching
☐ _____
☐ _____
☐ _____
☐ _____
☐ _____

RESERVATION INFORMATION:

Address: _____
_____

Reserved dates: _____

Check-in time: _____ Early check-in?: ☐ y ☐ n

Check-out time: _____ Late check-out?: ☐ y ☐ n

Website: _____

Phone: _____

WiFi: _____ WiFi password: _____

Dog friendly?: ☐ y ☐ n   Open all year?: ☐ y ☐ n

Traveling by:

☐ ☐ ☐ ☐ ☐ ☐ ☐ ☐ ☐ ☐ ☐ ☐

Add your favorite ticket stub, postcard, photo, stamp or drawing here

LET NEW ADVENTURES
»» BEGIN →

Montara State Beach

County: San Mateo

Established: 1959

Acres: 780

Star Rating
☆ ☆ ☆ ☆ ☆

My favorite thing about this place is... _____

Why I went ... _____

Who I went with ... _____

When I went ... _____

What I did... _____

What I saw... _____

What I learned... _____

An unforgettable moment... _____

A laughable moment... _____

A surprising moment... _____

An unforeseeable moment... _____

Wildlife spotted... _____

📷 Snapped a selfie | Location... _____

📷 Took a park sign photo? - ☐ y ☐ n

The weather was ... ☐ ☐ ☐ ☐ ☐ ☐ ☐

List
☐ _____
☐ _____
☐ _____
☐ _____
☐ _____
☐ _____
☐ _____
☐ _____
☐ _____
☐ _____
☐ _____
☐ _____
☐ _____
☐ _____
☐ _____
☐ _____
☐ _____
☐ _____
☐ _____

PLAN YOUR TRIP:

☐ Day Trip   ☐ Overnight Stay

Reservations required: ☐ y ☐ n

Date reservations made: _____

Refund Policy: ☐ y ☐ n Site #: _____

Confirmation #: _____

Miles to travel: _____

Time traveling: _____

RV's?: ☐ y ☐ n Largest size RV? _____

Activities Accomplished:

☐ Archery
☐ Biking
☐ Birding
☐ Boating
☐ Camping
☐ Caving
☐ Geocaching

☐ Fishing
☐ Hiking
☐ Horseback Riding
☐ Hunting
☐ Off-Roading
☐ Paddle Boarding
☐ Photography

☐ Picknicking
☐ Rock Climbing
☐ Shooting Range
☐ Snowshoeing
☐ Stargazing
☐ Swimming
☐ Tennis

☐ Walking
☐ Wildlife Watching
☐ _____
☐ _____
☐ _____
☐ _____
☐ _____

Traveling by:

☐ ☐ ☐ ☐ ☐ ☐ ☐ ☐ ☐ ☐ ☐ ☐

RESERVATION INFORMATION:

Address: _____
_____

Reserved dates: _____

Check-in time: _____ Early check-in?: ☐ y ☐ n

Check-out time: _____ Late check-out?: ☐ y ☐ n

Website: _____

Phone: _____

WiFi: _____ WiFi password: _____

Dog friendly?: ☐ y ☐ n   Open all year?: ☐ y ☐ n

Add your favorite ticket stub, postcard, photo, stamp or drawing here

LET NEW ADVENTURES
≫ BEGIN →

Monterey State Beach

County: Monterey

Established: 1960

Acres: 114

Star Rating
☆☆☆☆☆

My favorite thing about this place is... _____

Why I went ... _____

Who I went with ... _____

When I went ... _____

What I did... _____

What I saw... _____

What I learned... _____

An unforgettable moment... _____

A laughable moment... _____

A surprising moment... _____

An unforeseeable moment... _____

Wildlife spotted... _____

List

- ☐ _____
- ☐ _____
- ☐ _____
- ☐ _____
- ☐ _____
- ☐ _____
- ☐ _____
- ☐ _____
- ☐ _____
- ☐ _____
- ☐ _____
- ☐ _____
- ☐ _____
- ☐ _____
- ☐ _____
- ☐ _____
- ☐ _____
- ☐ _____
- ☐ _____

Snapped a selfie | Location... _____

Took a park sign photo? - ☐ y ☐ n

The weather was ...
☐ ☐ ☐ ☐ ☐ ☐ ☐

PLAN YOUR TRIP:

☐ Day Trip   ☐ Overnight Stay

Reservations required: ☐ y ☐ n

Date reservations made: _____

Refund Policy: ☐ y ☐ n Site #: _____

Confirmation #: _____

Miles to travel: _____

Time traveling: _____

RV's?: ☐ y ☐ n Largest size RV? _____

Activities Accomplished:

☐ Archery	☐ Fishing	☐ Picknicking	☐ Walking
☐ Biking	☐ Hiking	☐ Rock Climbing	☐ Wildlife Watching
☐ Birding	☐ Horseback Riding	☐ Shooting Range	☐ _____
☐ Boating	☐ Hunting	☐ Snowshoeing	☐ _____
☐ Camping	☐ Off-Roading	☐ Stargazing	☐ _____
☐ Caving	☐ Paddle Boarding	☐ Swimming	☐ _____
☐ Geocaching	☐ Photography	☐ Tennis	☐ _____

Traveling by:

☐ ☐ ☐ ☐ ☐ ☐ ☐ ☐ ☐ ☐ ☐ ☐

RESERVATION INFORMATION:

Address: _____
_____

Reserved dates: _____

Check-in time: _____ Early check-in?: ☐ y ☐ n

Check-out time: _____ Late check-out?: ☐ y ☐ n

Website: _____

Phone: _____

WiFi: _____ WiFi password: _____

Dog friendly?: ☐ y ☐ n   Open all year?: ☐ y ☐ n

Add your favorite ticket stub, postcard, photo, stamp or drawing here

LET NEW ADVENTURES
≫ BEGIN →

Moonlight State Beach

County: San Diego

Established: 1949

Acres: 15

Star Rating

☆ ☆ ☆ ☆ ☆

My favorite thing about this place is... _____

Why I went ... _____

Who I went with ... _____

When I went ... _____

What I did... _____

What I saw... _____

What I learned... _____

An unforgettable moment... _____

A laughable moment... _____

A surprising moment... _____

An unforeseeable moment... _____

Wildlife spotted... _____

List

- [ ] _____
- [ ] _____
- [ ] _____
- [ ] _____
- [ ] _____
- [ ] _____
- [ ] _____
- [ ] _____
- [ ] _____
- [ ] _____
- [ ] _____
- [ ] _____
- [ ] _____
- [ ] _____
- [ ] _____
- [ ] _____
- [ ] _____
- [ ] _____

Snapped a selfie | Location... _____

Took a park sign photo? - ☐ y ☐ n

The weather was ... ☐ ☐ ☐ ☐ ☐ ☐ ☐

PLAN YOUR TRIP:

☐ Day Trip   ☐ Overnight Stay

Reservations required: ☐ y ☐ n

Date reservations made: _____

Refund Policy: ☐ y ☐ n Site #: _____

Confirmation #: _____

Miles to travel: _____

Time traveling: _____

RV's?: ☐ y ☐ n Largest size RV? _____

Activities Accomplished:

☐ Archery	☐ Fishing	☐ Picknicking	☐ Walking
☐ Biking	☐ Hiking	☐ Rock Climbing	☐ Wildlife Watching
☐ Birding	☐ Horseback Riding	☐ Shooting Range	☐ _____
☐ Boating	☐ Hunting	☐ Snowshoeing	☐ _____
☐ Camping	☐ Off-Roading	☐ Stargazing	☐ _____
☐ Caving	☐ Paddle Boarding	☐ Swimming	☐ _____
☐ Geocaching	☐ Photography	☐ Tennis	☐ _____

Traveling by:

☐ ☐ ☐ ☐ ☐ ☐ ☐ ☐ ☐ ☐ ☐ ☐

RESERVATION INFORMATION:

Address: _____
_____

Reserved dates: _____

Check-in time: _____ Early check-in?: ☐ y ☐ n

Check-out time: _____ Late check-out?: ☐ y ☐ n

Website: _____

Phone: _____

WiFi: _____ WiFi password: _____

Dog friendly?: ☐ y ☐ n   Open all year?: ☐ y ☐ n

Add your favorite ticket stub, postcard, photo, stamp or drawing here

LET NEW ADVENTURES
≫ BEGIN →

Morro Strand State Beach

County: San Luis Obispo

Established: 1932

Acres: 183

_____
Star Rating
☆ ☆ ☆ ☆ ☆

My favorite thing about this place is... _____

Why I went ... _____

Who I went with ... _____

When I went ... _____

What I did... _____

What I saw... _____

What I learned... _____

An unforgettable moment... _____

A laughable moment... _____

A surprising moment... _____

An unforeseeable moment... _____

Wildlife spotted... _____

List
- [ ] _____
- [ ] _____
- [ ] _____
- [ ] _____
- [ ] _____
- [ ] _____
- [ ] _____
- [ ] _____
- [ ] _____
- [ ] _____
- [ ] _____
- [ ] _____
- [ ] _____
- [ ] _____
- [ ] _____
- [ ] _____
- [ ] _____
- [ ] _____

Snapped a selfie | Location... _____

Took a park sign photo? - ☐ y ☐ n

The weather was ...
☐ ☐ ☐ ☐ ☐ ☐ ☐

PLAN YOUR TRIP:

☐ Day Trip   ☐ Overnight Stay

Reservations required: ☐ y ☐ n

Date reservations made: _____

Refund Policy: ☐ y ☐ n Site #: _____

Confirmation #: _____

Miles to travel: _____

Time traveling: _____

RV's?: ☐ y ☐ n Largest size RV? _____

Activities Accomplished:

☐ Archery
☐ Biking
☐ Birding
☐ Boating
☐ Camping
☐ Caving
☐ Geocaching

☐ Fishing
☐ Hiking
☐ Horseback Riding
☐ Hunting
☐ Off-Roading
☐ Paddle Boarding
☐ Photography

☐ Picknicking
☐ Rock Climbing
☐ Shooting Range
☐ Snowshoeing
☐ Stargazing
☐ Swimming
☐ Tennis

☐ Walking
☐ Wildlife Watching
☐ _____
☐ _____
☐ _____
☐ _____
☐ _____

RESERVATION INFORMATION:

Address: _____
_____

Reserved dates: _____

Check-in time: _____ Early check-in?: ☐ y ☐ n

Check-out time: _____ Late check-out?: ☐ y ☐ n

Website: _____

Phone: _____

WiFi: _____ WiFi password: _____

Dog friendly?: ☐ y ☐ n   Open all year?: ☐ y ☐ n

Traveling by:

☐ ☐ ☐ ☐ ☐ ☐ ☐ ☐ ☐ ☐ ☐ ☐

Add your favorite ticket stub, postcard, photo, stamp or drawing here

LET NEW ADVENTURES
≫ BEGIN →

MOSS LANDING STATE BEACH

County: Monterey

Established: 1972

Acres: 60

_____
Star Rating
☆ ☆ ☆ ☆ ☆

My favorite thing about this place is... _____

Why I went ... _____

Who I went with ... _____

When I went ... _____

What I did... _____

What I saw... _____

_____

What I learned... _____

_____

An unforgettable moment... _____

_____

_____

A laughable moment... _____

_____

A surprising moment... _____

_____

An unforeseeable moment... _____

_____

Wildlife spotted... _____

📷 Snapped a selfie | Location... _____

📷 Took a park sign photo? - ☐ y ☐ n

List
- ☐ _____
- ☐ _____
- ☐ _____
- ☐ _____
- ☐ _____
- ☐ _____
- ☐ _____
- ☐ _____
- ☐ _____
- ☐ _____
- ☐ _____
- ☐ _____
- ☐ _____
- ☐ _____
- ☐ _____
- ☐ _____
- ☐ _____
- ☐ _____
- ☐ _____
- ☐ _____

The weather was ... ☐ ☐ ☐ ☐ ☐ ☐ ☐

PLAN YOUR TRIP:

☐ Day Trip   ☐ Overnight Stay

Reservations required: ☐ y ☐ n

Date reservations made: _____

Refund Policy: ☐ y ☐ n   Site #: _____

Confirmation #: _____

Miles to travel: _____

Time traveling: _____

RV's?: ☐ y ☐ n Largest size RV? _____

Activities Accomplished:

☐ Archery	☐ Fishing	☐ Picknicking	☐ Walking
☐ Biking	☐ Hiking	☐ Rock Climbing	☐ Wildlife Watching
☐ Birding	☐ Horseback Riding	☐ Shooting Range	☐ _____
☐ Boating	☐ Hunting	☐ Snowshoeing	☐ _____
☐ Camping	☐ Off-Roading	☐ Stargazing	☐ _____
☐ Caving	☐ Paddle Boarding	☐ Swimming	☐ _____
☐ Geocaching	☐ Photography	☐ Tennis	☐ _____

RESERVATION INFORMATION:

Address: _____
_____

Reserved dates: _____

Check-in time: _____   Early check-in?: ☐ y ☐ n

Check-out time: _____   Late check-out?: ☐ y ☐ n

Website: _____

Phone: _____

WiFi: _____   WiFi password: _____

Dog friendly?: ☐ y ☐ n   Open all year?: ☐ y ☐ n

Traveling by:

☐ ☐ ☐ ☐ ☐ ☐ ☐ ☐ ☐ ☐ ☐ ☐

Add your favorite ticket stub, postcard, photo, stamp or drawing here

LET NEW ADVENTURES
≫ BEGIN →

Natural Bridges State Beach

County: Santa Cruz

Established: 1933   *Acres:* 62

Star Rating
☆ ☆ ☆ ☆ ☆

My favorite thing about this place is... _____

Why I went ... _____

Who I went with ... _____

When I went ... _____

What I did... _____

What I saw... _____

What I learned... _____

An unforgettable moment... _____

A laughable moment... _____

A surprising moment... _____

An unforeseeable moment... _____

Wildlife spotted... _____

Snapped a selfie | Location... _____

Took a park sign photo? - ☐ y ☐ n

The weather was ... ☐ ☐ ☐ ☐ ☐ ☐ ☐

List
- ☐ _____
- ☐ _____
- ☐ _____
- ☐ _____
- ☐ _____
- ☐ _____
- ☐ _____
- ☐ _____
- ☐ _____
- ☐ _____
- ☐ _____
- ☐ _____
- ☐ _____
- ☐ _____
- ☐ _____
- ☐ _____
- ☐ _____
- ☐ _____
- ☐ _____

PLAN YOUR TRIP:

☐ Day Trip   ☐ Overnight Stay

Reservations required: ☐ y ☐ n

Date reservations made: _____

Refund Policy: ☐ y ☐ n Site #: _____

Confirmation #: _____

Miles to travel: _____

Time traveling: _____

RV's?: ☐ y ☐ n Largest size RV? _____

Activities Accomplished:

☐ Archery
☐ Biking
☐ Birding
☐ Boating
☐ Camping
☐ Caving
☐ Geocaching

☐ Fishing
☐ Hiking
☐ Horseback Riding
☐ Hunting
☐ Off-Roading
☐ Paddle Boarding
☐ Photography

☐ Picknicking
☐ Rock Climbing
☐ Shooting Range
☐ Snowshoeing
☐ Stargazing
☐ Swimming
☐ Tennis

☐ Walking
☐ Wildlife Watching
☐ _____
☐ _____
☐ _____
☐ _____
☐ _____

RESERVATION INFORMATION:

Address: _____
_____

Reserved dates: _____

Check-in time: _____ Early check-in?: ☐ y ☐ n

Check-out time: _____ Late check-out?: ☐ y ☐ n

Website: _____

Phone: _____

WiFi: _____ WiFi password: _____

Dog friendly?: ☐ y ☐ n   Open all year?: ☐ y ☐ n

Traveling by:

☐ ☐ ☐ ☐ ☐ ☐ ☐ ☐ ☐ ☐ ☐ ☐

Add your favorite ticket stub, postcard, photo, stamp or drawing here

LET NEW ADVENTURES
»» BEGIN →

NEW BRIGHTON STATE BEACH

County: Santa Cruz

Established: 1933   *Acres: 157*

Star Rating
☆ ☆ ☆ ☆ ☆

My favorite thing about this place is... _____

Why I went ... _____

Who I went with ... _____

When I went ... _____

What I did... _____

What I saw... _____

What I learned... _____

An unforgettable moment... _____

A laughable moment... _____

A surprising moment... _____

An unforeseeable moment... _____

Wildlife spotted... _____

List

☐ _____
☐ _____
☐ _____
☐ _____
☐ _____
☐ _____
☐ _____
☐ _____
☐ _____
☐ _____
☐ _____
☐ _____
☐ _____
☐ _____
☐ _____
☐ _____
☐ _____
☐ _____
☐ _____
☐ _____

Snapped a selfie | Location... _____

Took a park sign photo? - ☐ y ☐ n

The weather was ... ☐ ☐ ☐ ☐ ☐ ☐ ☐

PLAN YOUR TRIP:

☐ Day Trip   ☐ Overnight Stay

Reservations required: ☐ y ☐ n

Date reservations made: _____

Refund Policy: ☐ y ☐ n Site #: _____

Confirmation #: _____

Miles to travel: _____

Time traveling: _____

RV's?: ☐ y ☐ n Largest size RV? _____

Activities Accomplished:

☐ Archery   ☐ Fishing   ☐ Picknicking   ☐ Walking
☐ Biking   ☐ Hiking   ☐ Rock Climbing   ☐ Wildlife Watching
☐ Birding   ☐ Horseback Riding   ☐ Shooting Range   ☐ _____
☐ Boating   ☐ Hunting   ☐ Snowshoeing   ☐ _____
☐ Camping   ☐ Off-Roading   ☐ Stargazing   ☐ _____
☐ Caving   ☐ Paddle Boarding   ☐ Swimming   ☐ _____
☐ Geocaching   ☐ Photography   ☐ Tennis   ☐ _____

RESERVATION INFORMATION:

Address: _____
_____

Reserved dates: _____

Check-in time: _____ Early check-in?: ☐ y ☐ n

Check-out time: _____ Late check-out?: ☐ y ☐ n

Website: _____

Phone: _____

WiFi: _____ WiFi password: _____

Dog friendly?: ☐ y ☐ n   Open all year?: ☐ y ☐ n

Traveling by:

☐ ☐ ☐ ☐ ☐ ☐ ☐ ☐ ☐ ☐ ☐ ☐

Add your favorite ticket stub, postcard, photo, stamp or drawing here

LET NEW ADVENTURES
»» BEGIN →

Pacifica State Beach

County: San Mateo

Established: 1979   *Acres: 21*

Star Rating

☆☆☆☆☆

My favorite thing about this place is... _____

Why I went ... _____

Who I went with ... _____

When I went ... _____

What I did... _____

What I saw... _____

What I learned... _____

An unforgettable moment... _____

A laughable moment... _____

A surprising moment... _____

An unforeseeable moment... _____

Wildlife spotted... _____

Snapped a selfie | Location... _____

Took a park sign photo? - ☐ y ☐ n

The weather was ...

List

- ☐ _____
- ☐ _____
- ☐ _____
- ☐ _____
- ☐ _____
- ☐ _____
- ☐ _____
- ☐ _____
- ☐ _____
- ☐ _____
- ☐ _____
- ☐ _____
- ☐ _____
- ☐ _____
- ☐ _____
- ☐ _____
- ☐ _____
- ☐ _____
- ☐ _____

PLAN YOUR TRIP:

☐ Day Trip   ☐ Overnight Stay

Reservations required: ☐ y ☐ n

Date reservations made: _____

Refund Policy: ☐ y ☐ n Site #: _____

Confirmation #: _____

Miles to travel: _____

Time traveling: _____

RV's?: ☐ y ☐ n Largest size RV? _____

Activities Accomplished:

☐ Archery
☐ Biking
☐ Birding
☐ Boating
☐ Camping
☐ Caving
☐ Geocaching

☐ Fishing
☐ Hiking
☐ Horseback Riding
☐ Hunting
☐ Off-Roading
☐ Paddle Boarding
☐ Photography

☐ Picknicking
☐ Rock Climbing
☐ Shooting Range
☐ Snowshoeing
☐ Stargazing
☐ Swimming
☐ Tennis

☐ Walking
☐ Wildlife Watching
☐ _____
☐ _____
☐ _____
☐ _____
☐ _____

RESERVATION INFORMATION:

Address: _____
_____

Reserved dates: _____

Check-in time: _____ Early check-in?: ☐ y ☐ n

Check-out time: _____ Late check-out?: ☐ y ☐ n

Website: _____

Phone: _____

WiFi: _____ WiFi password: _____

Dog friendly?: ☐ y ☐ n   Open all year?: ☐ y ☐ n

Traveling by:

☐ ☐ ☐ ☐ ☐ ☐ ☐ ☐ ☐ ☐ ☐ ☐

Add your favorite ticket stub, postcard, photo, stamp or drawing here

LET NEW ADVENTURES
≫ BEGIN →

PELICAN STATE BEACH

County: Del Norte

Established: 1947

Acres: 5.2

Star Rating

☆ ☆ ☆ ☆ ☆

My favorite thing about this place is...

Why I went ...

Who I went with ...

When I went ...

What I did...

What I saw...

What I learned...

An unforgettable moment...

A laughable moment...

A surprising moment...

An unforeseeable moment...

Wildlife spotted...

List

- ☐
- ☐
- ☐
- ☐
- ☐
- ☐
- ☐
- ☐
- ☐
- ☐
- ☐
- ☐
- ☐
- ☐
- ☐
- ☐
- ☐
- ☐
- ☐
- ☐

Snapped a selfie | Location...

Took a park sign photo? - ☐ y ☐ n

The weather was ...
☐ ☐ ☐ ☐ ☐ ☐ ☐

PLAN YOUR TRIP:

☐ Day Trip   ☐ Overnight Stay

Reservations required: ☐ y ☐ n

Date reservations made: _____

Refund Policy: ☐ y ☐ n Site #: _____

Confirmation #: _____

Miles to travel: _____

Time traveling: _____

RV's?: ☐ y ☐ n Largest size RV? _____

Activities Accomplished:

☐ Archery
☐ Biking
☐ Birding
☐ Boating
☐ Camping
☐ Caving
☐ Geocaching

☐ Fishing
☐ Hiking
☐ Horseback Riding
☐ Hunting
☐ Off-Roading
☐ Paddle Boarding
☐ Photography

☐ Picknicking
☐ Rock Climbing
☐ Shooting Range
☐ Snowshoeing
☐ Stargazing
☐ Swimming
☐ Tennis

☐ Walking
☐ Wildlife Watching
☐ _____
☐ _____
☐ _____
☐ _____
☐ _____

RESERVATION INFORMATION:

Address: _____
_____

Reserved dates: _____

Check-in time: _____ Early check-in?: ☐ y ☐ n

Check-out time: _____ Late check-out?: ☐ y ☐ n

Website: _____

Phone: _____

WiFi: _____ WiFi password: _____

Dog friendly?: ☐ y ☐ n   Open all year?: ☐ y ☐ n

Traveling by:

☐ ☐ ☐ ☐ ☐ ☐ ☐ ☐ ☐ ☐ ☐ ☐

Add your favorite ticket stub, postcard, photo, stamp or drawing here

LET NEW ADVENTURES
»» BEGIN →

Pescadero State Beach

County: San Mateo

Established: 1958

Acres: 700

Star Rating

☆ ☆ ☆ ☆ ☆

My favorite thing about this place is... _____

Why I went ... _____

Who I went with ... _____

When I went ... _____

What I did... _____

What I saw... _____

What I learned... _____

An unforgettable moment... _____

A laughable moment... _____

A surprising moment... _____

An unforeseeable moment... _____

Wildlife spotted... _____

List

- [ ] _____
- [ ] _____
- [ ] _____
- [ ] _____
- [ ] _____
- [ ] _____
- [ ] _____
- [ ] _____
- [ ] _____
- [ ] _____
- [ ] _____
- [ ] _____
- [ ] _____
- [ ] _____
- [ ] _____
- [ ] _____
- [ ] _____
- [ ] _____

Snapped a selfie | Location... _____

Took a park sign photo? - ☐ y ☐ n

The weather was ...

PLAN YOUR TRIP:

☐ Day Trip   ☐ Overnight Stay

Reservations required: ☐ y ☐ n

Date reservations made: _____

Refund Policy: ☐ y ☐ n   Site #: _____

Confirmation #: _____

Miles to travel: _____

Time traveling: _____

RV's?: ☐ y ☐ n Largest size RV? _____

Activities Accomplished:

☐ Archery	☐ Fishing	☐ Picknicking	☐ Walking
☐ Biking	☐ Hiking	☐ Rock Climbing	☐ Wildlife Watching
☐ Birding	☐ Horseback Riding	☐ Shooting Range	☐ _____
☐ Boating	☐ Hunting	☐ Snowshoeing	☐ _____
☐ Camping	☐ Off-Roading	☐ Stargazing	☐ _____
☐ Caving	☐ Paddle Boarding	☐ Swimming	☐ _____
☐ Geocaching	☐ Photography	☐ Tennis	☐ _____

Traveling by:

☐ ☐ ☐ ☐ ☐ ☐ ☐ ☐ ☐ ☐ ☐ ☐

RESERVATION INFORMATION:

Address: _____
_____

Reserved dates: _____

Check-in time: _____   Early check-in?: ☐ y ☐ n

Check-out time: _____   Late check-out?: ☐ y ☐ n

Website: _____

Phone: _____

WiFi: _____   WiFi password: _____

Dog friendly?: ☐ y ☐ n   Open all year?: ☐ y ☐ n

Add your favorite ticket stub, postcard, photo, stamp or drawing here

LET NEW ADVENTURES
≫ BEGIN →

Pismo State Beach

County: San Luis Obispo

Established: 1935

Acres: 1,412

Star Rating

☆ ☆ ☆ ☆ ☆

My favorite thing about this place is... _____

Why I went ... _____

Who I went with ... _____

When I went ... _____

What I did... _____

What I saw... _____

What I learned... _____

An unforgettable moment... _____

A laughable moment... _____

A surprising moment... _____

An unforeseeable moment... _____

Wildlife spotted... _____

List

- ☐ _____
- ☐ _____
- ☐ _____
- ☐ _____
- ☐ _____
- ☐ _____
- ☐ _____
- ☐ _____
- ☐ _____
- ☐ _____
- ☐ _____
- ☐ _____
- ☐ _____
- ☐ _____
- ☐ _____
- ☐ _____
- ☐ _____
- ☐ _____

Snapped a selfie | Location... _____

Took a park sign photo? - ☐ y ☐ n

The weather was ...
☐ ☐ ☐ ☐ ☐ ☐ ☐

PLAN YOUR TRIP:

☐ Day Trip   ☐ Overnight Stay

Reservations required: ☐ y ☐ n

Date reservations made: _____

Refund Policy: ☐ y ☐ n Site #: _____

Confirmation #: _____

Miles to travel: _____

Time traveling: _____

RV's?: ☐ y ☐ n Largest size RV? _____

Activities Accomplished:

☐ Archery
☐ Biking
☐ Birding
☐ Boating
☐ Camping
☐ Caving
☐ Geocaching

☐ Fishing
☐ Hiking
☐ Horseback Riding
☐ Hunting
☐ Off-Roading
☐ Paddle Boarding
☐ Photography

☐ Picknicking
☐ Rock Climbing
☐ Shooting Range
☐ Snowshoeing
☐ Stargazing
☐ Swimming
☐ Tennis

☐ Walking
☐ Wildlife Watching
☐ _____
☐ _____
☐ _____
☐ _____
☐ _____

RESERVATION INFORMATION:

Address: _____
_____

Reserved dates: _____

Check-in time: _____   Early check-in?: ☐ y ☐ n

Check-out time: _____   Late check-out?: ☐ y ☐ n

Website: _____

Phone: _____

WiFi: _____   WiFi password: _____

Dog friendly?: ☐ y ☐ n   Open all year?: ☐ y ☐ n

Traveling by:

☐ ☐ ☐ ☐ ☐ ☐ ☐ ☐ ☐ ☐ ☐ ☐

Add your favorite ticket stub, postcard, photo, stamp or drawing here

LET NEW ADVENTURES
≫ BEGIN →

POINT DUME STATE BEACH

County: Los Angeles

Established: 1958

Acres: 37

Star Rating
☆☆☆☆☆

My favorite thing about this place is... _____

Why I went ... _____

Who I went with ... _____

When I went ... _____

What I did... _____

What I saw... _____

What I learned... _____

An unforgettable moment... _____

A laughable moment... _____

A surprising moment... _____

An unforeseeable moment... _____

Wildlife spotted... _____

Snapped a selfie | Location... _____

Took a park sign photo? - ☐ y ☐ n

List

☐ _____
☐ _____
☐ _____
☐ _____
☐ _____
☐ _____
☐ _____
☐ _____
☐ _____
☐ _____
☐ _____
☐ _____
☐ _____
☐ _____
☐ _____
☐ _____
☐ _____
☐ _____
☐ _____

The weather was ...
☐ ☐ ☐ ☐ ☐ ☐ ☐

PLAN YOUR TRIP:

☐ Day Trip   ☐ Overnight Stay

Reservations required: ☐ y ☐ n

Date reservations made: _____

Refund Policy: ☐ y ☐ n   Site #: _____

Confirmation #: _____

Miles to travel: _____

Time traveling: _____

RV's?: ☐ y ☐ n Largest size RV? _____

Activities Accomplished:

☐ Archery	☐ Fishing	☐ Picknicking	☐ Walking
☐ Biking	☐ Hiking	☐ Rock Climbing	☐ Wildlife Watching
☐ Birding	☐ Horseback Riding	☐ Shooting Range	☐ _____
☐ Boating	☐ Hunting	☐ Snowshoeing	☐ _____
☐ Camping	☐ Off-Roading	☐ Stargazing	☐ _____
☐ Caving	☐ Paddle Boarding	☐ Swimming	☐ _____
☐ Geocaching	☐ Photography	☐ Tennis	☐ _____

RESERVATION INFORMATION:

Address: _____
_____

Reserved dates: _____

Check-in time: _____   Early check-in?: ☐ y ☐ n

Check-out time: _____   Late check-out?: ☐ y ☐ n

Website: _____

Phone: _____

WiFi: _____   WiFi password: _____

Dog friendly?: ☐ y ☐ n   Open all year?: ☐ y ☐ n

Traveling by:

☐ ☐ ☐ ☐ ☐ ☐ ☐ ☐ ☐ ☐ ☐ ☐

Add your favorite ticket stub, postcard, photo, stamp or drawing here

LET NEW ADVENTURES
>> BEGIN →

POINT SAL STATE BEACH

County: Santa Barbara

Established: 1948   *Acres: 84*

Star Rating
☆ ☆ ☆ ☆ ☆

My favorite thing about this place is... _____

Why I went ... _____

Who I went with ... _____

When I went ... _____

What I did... _____

What I saw... _____

What I learned... _____

An unforgettable moment... _____

A laughable moment... _____

A surprising moment... _____

An unforeseeable moment... _____

Wildlife spotted... _____

List
- [ ] _____
- [ ] _____
- [ ] _____
- [ ] _____
- [ ] _____
- [ ] _____
- [ ] _____
- [ ] _____
- [ ] _____
- [ ] _____
- [ ] _____
- [ ] _____
- [ ] _____
- [ ] _____
- [ ] _____
- [ ] _____
- [ ] _____
- [ ] _____

Snapped a selfie | Location... _____

Took a park sign photo? - ☐ y ☐ n

The weather was ... ☐ ☐ ☐ ☐ ☐ ☐ ☐

PLAN YOUR TRIP:

☐ Day Trip   ☐ Overnight Stay

Reservations required: ☐y ☐n

Date reservations made: _____

Refund Policy: ☐y ☐n Site #: _____

Confirmation #: _____

Miles to travel: _____

Time traveling: _____

RV's?: ☐y ☐n Largest size RV? _____

Activities Accomplished:

☐ Archery
☐ Biking
☐ Birding
☐ Boating
☐ Camping
☐ Caving
☐ Geocaching

☐ Fishing
☐ Hiking
☐ Horseback Riding
☐ Hunting
☐ Off-Roading
☐ Paddle Boarding
☐ Photography

☐ Picknicking
☐ Rock Climbing
☐ Shooting Range
☐ Snowshoeing
☐ Stargazing
☐ Swimming
☐ Tennis

☐ Walking
☐ Wildlife Watching
☐ _____
☐ _____
☐ _____
☐ _____
☐ _____

RESERVATION INFORMATION:

Address: _____
_____

Reserved dates: _____

Check-in time: _____ Early check-in?: ☐y ☐n

Check-out time: _____ Late check-out?: ☐y ☐n

Website: _____

Phone: _____

WiFi: _____ WiFi password: _____

Dog friendly?: ☐y ☐n   Open all year?: ☐y ☐n

Traveling by:

☐ ☐ ☐ ☐ ☐ ☐ ☐ ☐ ☐ ☐ ☐ ☐

Add your favorite ticket stub, postcard, photo, stamp or drawing here

LET NEW ADVENTURES
»» BEGIN →

POMPONIO STATE BEACH

County: San Mateo

Established: 1960

Acres: 421

Star Rating
☆☆☆☆☆

My favorite thing about this place is... _____

Why I went ... _____

Who I went with ... _____

When I went ... _____

What I did... _____

What I saw... _____

What I learned... _____

An unforgettable moment... _____

A laughable moment... _____

A surprising moment... _____

An unforeseeable moment... _____

Wildlife spotted... _____

Snapped a selfie | Location... _____

Took a park sign photo? - ☐ y ☐ n

List
- ☐ _____
- ☐ _____
- ☐ _____
- ☐ _____
- ☐ _____
- ☐ _____
- ☐ _____
- ☐ _____
- ☐ _____
- ☐ _____
- ☐ _____
- ☐ _____
- ☐ _____
- ☐ _____
- ☐ _____
- ☐ _____
- ☐ _____
- ☐ _____
- ☐ _____
- ☐ _____
- ☐ _____

The weather was ...
☐ ☐ ☐ ☐ ☐ ☐ ☐

PLAN YOUR TRIP:

☐ Day Trip   ☐ Overnight Stay

Reservations required: ☐ y ☐ n

Date reservations made: _____

Refund Policy: ☐ y ☐ n   Site #: _____

Confirmation #: _____

Miles to travel: _____

Time traveling: _____

RV's?: ☐ y ☐ n Largest size RV? _____

Activities Accomplished:

☐ Archery
☐ Biking
☐ Birding
☐ Boating
☐ Camping
☐ Caving
☐ Geocaching

☐ Fishing
☐ Hiking
☐ Horseback Riding
☐ Hunting
☐ Off-Roading
☐ Paddle Boarding
☐ Photography

☐ Picknicking
☐ Rock Climbing
☐ Shooting Range
☐ Snowshoeing
☐ Stargazing
☐ Swimming
☐ Tennis

☐ Walking
☐ Wildlife Watching
☐ _____
☐ _____
☐ _____
☐ _____
☐ _____

Traveling by:

☐ ☐ ☐ ☐ ☐ ☐ ☐ ☐ ☐ ☐ ☐ ☐

RESERVATION INFORMATION:

Address: _____
_____

Reserved dates: _____

Check-in time: _____   Early check-in?: ☐ y ☐ n

Check-out time: _____   Late check-out?: ☐ y ☐ n

Website: _____

Phone: _____

WiFi: _____   WiFi password: _____

Dog friendly?: ☐ y ☐ n   Open all year?: ☐ y ☐ n

Add your favorite ticket stub, postcard, photo, stamp or drawing here

LET NEW ADVENTURES
»> BEGIN →

Refugio State Beach

County: Santa Barbara

Established: 1950

Acres: 905

_____
Star Rating
☆ ☆ ☆ ☆ ☆

My favorite thing about this place is... _____

Why I went ... _____

Who I went with ... _____

When I went ... _____

What I did... _____

What I saw... _____

What I learned... _____

An unforgettable moment... _____

A laughable moment... _____

A surprising moment... _____

An unforeseeable moment... _____

Wildlife spotted... _____

List
- ☐ _____
- ☐ _____
- ☐ _____
- ☐ _____
- ☐ _____
- ☐ _____
- ☐ _____
- ☐ _____
- ☐ _____
- ☐ _____
- ☐ _____
- ☐ _____
- ☐ _____
- ☐ _____
- ☐ _____
- ☐ _____
- ☐ _____

Snapped a selfie | Location... _____

Took a park sign photo? - ☐ y ☐ n

The weather was ...
☐ ☐ ☐ ☐ ☐ ☐ ☐

PLAN YOUR TRIP:

☐ Day Trip   ☐ Overnight Stay

Reservations required: ☐ y ☐ n

Date reservations made: _____

Refund Policy: ☐ y ☐ n   Site #: _____

Confirmation #: _____

Miles to travel: _____

Time traveling: _____

RV's?: ☐ y ☐ n Largest size RV? _____

Activities Accomplished:

☐ Archery
☐ Biking
☐ Birding
☐ Boating
☐ Camping
☐ Caving
☐ Geocaching

☐ Fishing
☐ Hiking
☐ Horseback Riding
☐ Hunting
☐ Off-Roading
☐ Paddle Boarding
☐ Photography

☐ Picknicking
☐ Rock Climbing
☐ Shooting Range
☐ Snowshoeing
☐ Stargazing
☐ Swimming
☐ Tennis

☐ Walking
☐ Wildlife Watching
☐ _____
☐ _____
☐ _____
☐ _____
☐ _____

Traveling by:

☐   ☐   ☐   ☐   ☐   ☐   ☐   ☐   ☐   ☐   ☐   ☐

RESERVATION INFORMATION:

Address: _____
_____

Reserved dates: _____

Check-in time: _____   Early check-in?: ☐ y ☐ n

Check-out time: _____   Late check-out?: ☐ y ☐ n

Website: _____

Phone: _____

WiFi: _____   WiFi password: _____

Dog friendly?: ☐ y ☐ n   Open all year?: ☐ y ☐ n

Add your favorite ticket stub, postcard, photo, stamp or drawing here

LET NEW ADVENTURES
»» BEGIN →

ROBERT H. MEYER MEMORIAL STATE BEACH

County: Los Angeles

Established: 1978   *Acres:* 37

Star Rating
☆ ☆ ☆ ☆ ☆

My favorite thing about this place is... _____

Why I went ... _____

Who I went with ... _____

When I went ... _____

What I did... _____

What I saw... _____

What I learned... _____

An unforgettable moment... _____

A laughable moment... _____

A surprising moment... _____

An unforeseeable moment... _____

Wildlife spotted... _____

List
- [ ] _____
- [ ] _____
- [ ] _____
- [ ] _____
- [ ] _____
- [ ] _____
- [ ] _____
- [ ] _____
- [ ] _____
- [ ] _____
- [ ] _____
- [ ] _____
- [ ] _____
- [ ] _____
- [ ] _____
- [ ] _____
- [ ] _____
- [ ] _____
- [ ] _____

Snapped a selfie | Location... _____

Took a park sign photo? - ☐ y ☐ n

The weather was ... ☐ ☐ ☐ ☐ ☐ ☐ ☐

PLAN YOUR TRIP:

☐ Day Trip   ☐ Overnight Stay

Reservations required: ☐ y ☐ n

Date reservations made: _____

Refund Policy: ☐ y ☐ n Site #: _____

Confirmation #: _____

Miles to travel: _____

Time traveling: _____

RV's?: ☐ y ☐ n Largest size RV? _____

Activities Accomplished:

☐ Archery
☐ Biking
☐ Birding
☐ Boating
☐ Camping
☐ Caving
☐ Geocaching

☐ Fishing
☐ Hiking
☐ Horseback Riding
☐ Hunting
☐ Off-Roading
☐ Paddle Boarding
☐ Photography

☐ Picknicking
☐ Rock Climbing
☐ Shooting Range
☐ Snowshoeing
☐ Stargazing
☐ Swimming
☐ Tennis

☐ Walking
☐ Wildlife Watching
☐ _____
☐ _____
☐ _____
☐ _____
☐ _____

Traveling by:

☐ ☐ ☐ ☐ ☐ ☐ ☐ ☐ ☐ ☐ ☐ ☐

RESERVATION INFORMATION:

Address: _____
_____

Reserved dates: _____

Check-in time: _____ Early check-in?: ☐ y ☐ n

Check-out time: _____ Late check-out?: ☐ y ☐ n

Website: _____

Phone: _____

WiFi: _____ WiFi password: _____

Dog friendly?: ☐ y ☐ n   Open all year?: ☐ y ☐ n

Add your favorite ticket stub, postcard, photo, stamp or drawing here

LET NEW ADVENTURES
≫ BEGIN →

ROBERT W. CROWN MEMORIAL STATE BEACH

County: Alameda

Established: 1961

Acres: 132

_____
Star Rating
☆ ☆ ☆ ☆ ☆

My favorite thing about this place is...

Why I went ...

Who I went with ...

When I went ...

What I did...

What I saw...

What I learned...

An unforgettable moment...

A laughable moment...

A surprising moment...

An unforeseeable moment...

Wildlife spotted...

Snapped a selfie | Location...

Took a park sign photo? - ☐ y ☐ n

List
- ☐
- ☐
- ☐
- ☐
- ☐
- ☐
- ☐
- ☐
- ☐
- ☐
- ☐
- ☐
- ☐
- ☐
- ☐
- ☐
- ☐
- ☐
- ☐

The weather was ...
☐ ☐ ☐ ☐ ☐ ☐ ☐

PLAN YOUR TRIP:

RESERVATION INFORMATION:

☐ Day Trip   ☐ Overnight Stay

Reservations required: ☐ y ☐ n

Date reservations made: _____

Refund Policy: ☐ y ☐ n Site #: _____

Confirmation #: _____

Miles to travel: _____

Time traveling: _____

RV's?: ☐ y ☐ n Largest size RV? _____

Address: _____
_____

Reserved dates: _____

Check-in time: _____ Early check-in?: ☐ y ☐ n

Check-out time: _____ Late check-out?: ☐ y ☐ n

Website: _____

Phone: _____

WiFi: _____ WiFi password: _____

Dog friendly?: ☐ y ☐ n   Open all year?: ☐ y ☐ n

Activities Accomplished:

☐ Archery
☐ Biking
☐ Birding
☐ Boating
☐ Camping
☐ Caving
☐ Geocaching

☐ Fishing
☐ Hiking
☐ Horseback Riding
☐ Hunting
☐ Off-Roading
☐ Paddle Boarding
☐ Photography

☐ Picknicking
☐ Rock Climbing
☐ Shooting Range
☐ Snowshoeing
☐ Stargazing
☐ Swimming
☐ Tennis

☐ Walking
☐ Wildlife Watching
☐ _____
☐ _____
☐ _____
☐ _____
☐ _____

Traveling by:

☐ ☐ ☐ ☐ ☐ ☐ ☐ ☐ ☐ ☐ ☐ ☐

Add your favorite ticket stub, postcard, photo, stamp or drawing here

LET NEW ADVENTURES
≫ BEGIN →

SALINAS RIVER STATE BEACH

County: Monterey and Santa Cruz

Established: 1960

Acres: 281.84

Star Rating
☆ ☆ ☆ ☆ ☆

My favorite thing about this place is...

Why I went ...

Who I went with ...

When I went ...

What I did...

What I saw...

What I learned...

An unforgettable moment...

A laughable moment...

A surprising moment...

An unforeseeable moment...

Wildlife spotted...

List

☐
☐
☐
☐
☐
☐
☐
☐
☐
☐
☐
☐
☐
☐
☐
☐
☐
☐
☐
☐

Snapped a selfie | Location...

Took a park sign photo? - ☐ y ☐ n

The weather was ...
☐ ☐ ☐ ☐ ☐ ☐ ☐

PLAN YOUR TRIP:

RESERVATION INFORMATION:

☐ Day Trip   ☐ Overnight Stay

Reservations required: ☐ y ☐ n

Date reservations made: _____

Refund Policy: ☐ y ☐ n Site #: _____

Confirmation #: _____

Miles to travel: _____

Time traveling: _____

RV's?: ☐ y ☐ n Largest size RV? _____

Activities Accomplished:

Address: _____
_____

Reserved dates: _____

Check-in time: _____ Early check-in?: ☐ y ☐ n

Check-out time: _____ Late check-out?: ☐ y ☐ n

Website: _____

Phone: _____

WiFi: _____ WiFi password: _____

Dog friendly?: ☐ y ☐ n   Open all year?: ☐ y ☐ n

☐ Archery	☐ Fishing	☐ Picknicking	☐ Walking
☐ Biking	☐ Hiking	☐ Rock Climbing	☐ Wildlife Watching
☐ Birding	☐ Horseback Riding	☐ Shooting Range	☐ _____
☐ Boating	☐ Hunting	☐ Snowshoeing	☐ _____
☐ Camping	☐ Off-Roading	☐ Stargazing	☐ _____
☐ Caving	☐ Paddle Boarding	☐ Swimming	☐ _____
☐ Geocaching	☐ Photography	☐ Tennis	☐ _____

Traveling by:

☐ ☐ ☐ ☐ ☐ ☐ ☐ ☐ ☐ ☐ ☐ ☐

Add your favorite ticket stub, postcard, photo, stamp or drawing here

LET NEW ADVENTURES
»» BEGIN →

SAN BUENAVENTURA STATE BEACH

County: Ventura

Established: 1961

Acres: 110

Star Rating
☆ ☆ ☆ ☆ ☆

My favorite thing about this place is...

Why I went ...

Who I went with ...

When I went ...

What I did...

What I saw...

What I learned...

An unforgettable moment...

A laughable moment...

A surprising moment...

An unforeseeable moment...

Wildlife spotted...

Snapped a selfie | Location...

Took a park sign photo? - ☐ y ☐ n

List
- ☐
- ☐
- ☐
- ☐
- ☐
- ☐
- ☐
- ☐
- ☐
- ☐
- ☐
- ☐
- ☐
- ☐
- ☐
- ☐
- ☐
- ☐
- ☐

The weather was ...
☐ ☐ ☐ ☐ ☐ ☐ ☐

PLAN YOUR TRIP:

RESERVATION INFORMATION:

☐ Day Trip   ☐ Overnight Stay

Reservations required: ☐ y ☐ n

Date reservations made: _____

Refund Policy: ☐ y ☐ n   Site #: _____

Confirmation #: _____

Miles to travel: _____

Time traveling: _____

RV's?: ☐ y ☐ n   Largest size RV? _____

Address: _____
_____

Reserved dates: _____

Check-in time: _____ Early check-in?: ☐ y ☐ n

Check-out time: _____ Late check-out?: ☐ y ☐ n

Website: _____

Phone: _____

WiFi: _____ WiFi password: _____

Dog friendly?: ☐ y ☐ n   Open all year?: ☐ y ☐ n

Activities Accomplished:

☐ Archery
☐ Biking
☐ Birding
☐ Boating
☐ Camping
☐ Caving
☐ Geocaching

☐ Fishing
☐ Hiking
☐ Horseback Riding
☐ Hunting
☐ Off-Roading
☐ Paddle Boarding
☐ Photography

☐ Picknicking
☐ Rock Climbing
☐ Shooting Range
☐ Snowshoeing
☐ Stargazing
☐ Swimming
☐ Tennis

☐ Walking
☐ Wildlife Watching
☐ _____
☐ _____
☐ _____
☐ _____
☐ _____

Traveling by:

☐   ☐   ☐   ☐   ☐   ☐   ☐   ☐   ☐   ☐   ☐   ☐

Add your favorite ticket stub, postcard, photo, stamp or drawing here

LET NEW ADVENTURES
≫ BEGIN →

San Clemente State Beach

County: Orange

Established: 1931

Acres: 117

Star Rating
☆ ☆ ☆ ☆ ☆

My favorite thing about this place is... _____

Why I went ... _____

Who I went with ... _____

When I went ... _____

What I did... _____

What I saw... _____

What I learned... _____

An unforgettable moment... _____

A laughable moment... _____

A surprising moment... _____

An unforeseeable moment... _____

Wildlife spotted... _____

List
- [ ] _____
- [ ] _____
- [ ] _____
- [ ] _____
- [ ] _____
- [ ] _____
- [ ] _____
- [ ] _____
- [ ] _____
- [ ] _____
- [ ] _____
- [ ] _____
- [ ] _____
- [ ] _____
- [ ] _____
- [ ] _____
- [ ] _____
- [ ] _____
- [ ] _____

Snapped a selfie | Location...

Took a park sign photo? - ☐ y ☐ n

The weather was ...
☐ ☐ ☐ ☐ ☐ ☐ ☐

PLAN YOUR TRIP:

☐ Day Trip   ☐ Overnight Stay

Reservations required: ☐ y ☐ n

Date reservations made: _____

Refund Policy: ☐ y ☐ n   Site #: _____

Confirmation #: _____

Miles to travel: _____

Time traveling: _____

RV's?: ☐ y ☐ n Largest size RV? _____

Activities Accomplished:

☐ Archery	☐ Fishing	☐ Picknicking	☐ Walking
☐ Biking	☐ Hiking	☐ Rock Climbing	☐ Wildlife Watching
☐ Birding	☐ Horseback Riding	☐ Shooting Range	☐ _____
☐ Boating	☐ Hunting	☐ Snowshoeing	☐ _____
☐ Camping	☐ Off-Roading	☐ Stargazing	☐ _____
☐ Caving	☐ Paddle Boarding	☐ Swimming	☐ _____
☐ Geocaching	☐ Photography	☐ Tennis	☐ _____

Traveling by:

☐   ☐   ☐   ☐   ☐   ☐   ☐   ☐   ☐   ☐   ☐   ☐

RESERVATION INFORMATION:

Address: _____
_____

Reserved dates: _____

Check-in time: _____   Early check-in?: ☐ y ☐ n

Check-out time: _____   Late check-out?: ☐ y ☐ n

Website: _____

Phone: _____

WiFi: _____   WiFi password: _____

Dog friendly?: ☐ y ☐ n   Open all year?: ☐ y ☐ n

Add your favorite ticket stub, postcard, photo, stamp or drawing here

LET NEW ADVENTURES
≫ BEGIN →

SAN ELIJO STATE BEACH

County: San Diego

Established: 1952

Acres: 588

_____
Star Rating
☆ ☆ ☆ ☆ ☆

My favorite thing about this place is... _____

Why I went ... _____

Who I went with ... _____

When I went ... _____

What I did... _____

What I saw... _____

What I learned... _____

An unforgettable moment... _____

A laughable moment... _____

A surprising moment... _____

An unforeseeable moment... _____

Wildlife spotted... _____

List

- [ ] _____
- [ ] _____
- [ ] _____
- [ ] _____
- [ ] _____
- [ ] _____
- [ ] _____
- [ ] _____
- [ ] _____
- [ ] _____
- [ ] _____
- [ ] _____
- [ ] _____
- [ ] _____
- [ ] _____
- [ ] _____
- [ ] _____
- [ ] _____
- [ ] _____

Snapped a selfie | Location... _____

Took a park sign photo? - ☐ y ☐ n

The weather was ...
☐ ☐ ☐ ☐ ☐ ☐ ☐

PLAN YOUR TRIP:

☐ Day Trip   ☐ Overnight Stay

Reservations required: ☐ y ☐ n

Date reservations made: _____

Refund Policy: ☐ y ☐ n Site #: _____

Confirmation #: _____

Miles to travel: _____

Time traveling: _____

RV's?: ☐ y ☐ n Largest size RV? _____

Activities Accomplished:

☐ Archery
☐ Biking
☐ Birding
☐ Boating
☐ Camping
☐ Caving
☐ Geocaching

☐ Fishing
☐ Hiking
☐ Horseback Riding
☐ Hunting
☐ Off-Roading
☐ Paddle Boarding
☐ Photography

☐ Picknicking
☐ Rock Climbing
☐ Shooting Range
☐ Snowshoeing
☐ Stargazing
☐ Swimming
☐ Tennis

☐ Walking
☐ Wildlife Watching
☐ _____
☐ _____
☐ _____
☐ _____
☐ _____

RESERVATION INFORMATION:

Address: _____
_____

Reserved dates: _____

Check-in time: _____ Early check-in?: ☐ y ☐ n

Check-out time: _____ Late check-out?: ☐ y ☐ n

Website: _____

Phone: _____

WiFi: _____ WiFi password: _____

Dog friendly?: ☐ y ☐ n   Open all year?: ☐ y ☐ n

Traveling by:

☐ ☐ ☐ ☐ ☐ ☐ ☐ ☐ ☐ ☐ ☐ ☐

Add your favorite ticket stub, postcard, photo, stamp or drawing here

LET NEW ADVENTURES
»» BEGIN →

SAN GREGORIO STATE BEACH

County: San Mateo

Established: 1958   *Acres: 414*

Star Rating
☆ ☆ ☆ ☆ ☆

My favorite thing about this place is... _____

Why I went ... _____

Who I went with ... _____

When I went ... _____

What I did... _____

What I saw... _____

What I learned... _____

An unforgettable moment... _____

A laughable moment... _____

A surprising moment... _____

An unforeseeable moment... _____

Wildlife spotted... _____

List
- ☐ _____
- ☐ _____
- ☐ _____
- ☐ _____
- ☐ _____
- ☐ _____
- ☐ _____
- ☐ _____
- ☐ _____
- ☐ _____
- ☐ _____
- ☐ _____
- ☐ _____
- ☐ _____
- ☐ _____
- ☐ _____
- ☐ _____
- ☐ _____

📷 Snapped a selfie | Location... _____

📷 Took a park sign photo? - ☐ y ☐ n

The weather was ...
☐ ☐ ☐ ☐ ☐ ☐ ☐

PLAN YOUR TRIP:

☐ Day Trip   ☐ Overnight Stay

Reservations required: ☐ y ☐ n

Date reservations made: _____

Refund Policy: ☐ y ☐ n Site #: _____

Confirmation #: _____

Miles to travel: _____

Time traveling: _____

RV's?: ☐ y ☐ n Largest size RV? _____

Activities Accomplished:

☐ Archery
☐ Biking
☐ Birding
☐ Boating
☐ Camping
☐ Caving
☐ Geocaching

☐ Fishing
☐ Hiking
☐ Horseback Riding
☐ Hunting
☐ Off-Roading
☐ Paddle Boarding
☐ Photography

☐ Picknicking
☐ Rock Climbing
☐ Shooting Range
☐ Snowshoeing
☐ Stargazing
☐ Swimming
☐ Tennis

☐ Walking
☐ Wildlife Watching
☐ _____
☐ _____
☐ _____
☐ _____
☐ _____

RESERVATION INFORMATION:

Address: _____
_____

Reserved dates: _____

Check-in time: _____ Early check-in?: ☐ y ☐ n

Check-out time: _____ Late check-out?: ☐ y ☐ n

Website: _____

Phone: _____

WiFi: _____ WiFi password: _____

Dog friendly?: ☐ y ☐ n   Open all year?: ☐ y ☐ n

Traveling by:

☐ ☐ ☐ ☐ ☐ ☐ ☐ ☐ ☐ ☐ ☐ ☐

Add your favorite ticket stub, postcard, photo, stamp or drawing here

LET NEW ADVENTURES
»» BEGIN →

SAN ONOFRE STATE BEACH

County: San Diego

Established: 1971

Acres: 2,107

Star Rating

☆ ☆ ☆ ☆ ☆

My favorite thing about this place is... _____

Why I went ... _____

Who I went with ... _____

When I went ... _____

What I did... _____

What I saw... _____

What I learned... _____

An unforgettable moment... _____

A laughable moment... _____

A surprising moment... _____

An unforeseeable moment... _____

Wildlife spotted... _____

List

- [ ] _____
- [ ] _____
- [ ] _____
- [ ] _____
- [ ] _____
- [ ] _____
- [ ] _____
- [ ] _____
- [ ] _____
- [ ] _____
- [ ] _____
- [ ] _____
- [ ] _____
- [ ] _____
- [ ] _____
- [ ] _____
- [ ] _____

Snapped a selfie | Location... _____

Took a park sign photo? - ☐ y ☐ n

The weather was ...

PLAN YOUR TRIP:

☐ Day Trip   ☐ Overnight Stay

Reservations required: ☐ y ☐ n

Date reservations made: _____

Refund Policy: ☐ y ☐ n Site #: _____

Confirmation #: _____

Miles to travel: _____

Time traveling: _____

RV's?: ☐ y ☐ n Largest size RV? _____

Activities Accomplished:

☐ Archery
☐ Biking
☐ Birding
☐ Boating
☐ Camping
☐ Caving
☐ Geocaching

☐ Fishing
☐ Hiking
☐ Horseback Riding
☐ Hunting
☐ Off-Roading
☐ Paddle Boarding
☐ Photography

☐ Picknicking
☐ Rock Climbing
☐ Shooting Range
☐ Snowshoeing
☐ Stargazing
☐ Swimming
☐ Tennis

☐ Walking
☐ Wildlife Watching
☐ _____
☐ _____
☐ _____
☐ _____
☐ _____

RESERVATION INFORMATION:

Address: _____
_____

Reserved dates: _____

Check-in time: _____   Early check-in?: ☐ y ☐ n

Check-out time: _____   Late check-out?: ☐ y ☐ n

Website: _____

Phone: _____

WiFi: _____   WiFi password: _____

Dog friendly?: ☐ y ☐ n   Open all year?: ☐ y ☐ n

Traveling by:

☐ ☐ ☐ ☐ ☐ ☐ ☐ ☐ ☐ ☐ ☐ ☐

Add your favorite ticket stub, postcard, photo, stamp or drawing here

LET NEW ADVENTURES
≫ BEGIN →

SANTA MONICA STATE BEACH

County: Los Angeles

Established: 1948

Acres: 48

Star Rating
☆☆☆☆☆

My favorite thing about this place is... _____

Why I went ... _____

Who I went with ... _____

When I went ... _____

What I did... _____

What I saw... _____

What I learned... _____

An unforgettable moment... _____

A laughable moment... _____

A surprising moment... _____

An unforeseeable moment... _____

Wildlife spotted... _____

List
- [ ] _____
- [ ] _____
- [ ] _____
- [ ] _____
- [ ] _____
- [ ] _____
- [ ] _____
- [ ] _____
- [ ] _____
- [ ] _____
- [ ] _____
- [ ] _____
- [ ] _____
- [ ] _____
- [ ] _____
- [ ] _____
- [ ] _____
- [ ] _____
- [ ] _____
- [ ] _____

Snapped a selfie | Location... _____

Took a park sign photo? - ☐ y ☐ n

The weather was ...
☐ ☐ ☐ ☐ ☐ ☐ ☐

PLAN YOUR TRIP:

☐ Day Trip   ☐ Overnight Stay

Reservations required: ☐y ☐n

Date reservations made: _____

Refund Policy: ☐y ☐n Site #: _____

Confirmation #: _____

Miles to travel: _____

Time traveling: _____

RV's?: ☐y ☐n Largest size RV? _____

Activities Accomplished:

☐ Archery
☐ Biking
☐ Birding
☐ Boating
☐ Camping
☐ Caving
☐ Geocaching

☐ Fishing
☐ Hiking
☐ Horseback Riding
☐ Hunting
☐ Off-Roading
☐ Paddle Boarding
☐ Photography

☐ Picknicking
☐ Rock Climbing
☐ Shooting Range
☐ Snowshoeing
☐ Stargazing
☐ Swimming
☐ Tennis

☐ Walking
☐ Wildlife Watching
☐ _____
☐ _____
☐ _____
☐ _____
☐ _____

Traveling by:

☐ ☐ ☐ ☐ ☐ ☐ ☐ ☐ ☐ ☐ ☐ ☐

RESERVATION INFORMATION:

Address: _____
_____

Reserved dates: _____

Check-in time: _____ Early check-in?: ☐y ☐n

Check-out time: _____ Late check-out?: ☐y ☐n

Website: _____

Phone: _____

WiFi: _____ WiFi password: _____

Dog friendly?: ☐y ☐n   Open all year?: ☐y ☐n

Add your favorite ticket stub, postcard, photo, stamp or drawing here

LET NEW ADVENTURES
»» BEGIN →

Schooner Gulch State Beach

County: Mendocino

Established: 1983   *Acres:* 54

Star Rating
☆ ☆ ☆ ☆ ☆

My favorite thing about this place is... _____

Why I went ... _____

Who I went with ... _____

When I went ... _____

What I did... _____

What I saw... _____

List
☐ _____
☐ _____
☐ _____
☐ _____
☐ _____
☐ _____
☐ _____
☐ _____
☐ _____
☐ _____
☐ _____
☐ _____
☐ _____
☐ _____
☐ _____
☐ _____
☐ _____
☐ _____

What I learned... _____

An unforgettable moment... _____

A laughable moment... _____

A surprising moment... _____

An unforeseeable moment... _____

Wildlife spotted... _____

Snapped a selfie | Location...

Took a park sign photo? - ☐ y ☐ n

The weather was ...
☐ ☐ ☐ ☐ ☐ ☐ ☐

PLAN YOUR TRIP:

☐ Day Trip   ☐ Overnight Stay

Reservations required: ☐ y ☐ n

Date reservations made: _____

Refund Policy: ☐ y ☐ n Site #: _____

Confirmation #: _____

Miles to travel: _____

Time traveling: _____

RV's?: ☐ y ☐ n Largest size RV? _____

Activities Accomplished:

☐ Archery
☐ Biking
☐ Birding
☐ Boating
☐ Camping
☐ Caving
☐ Geocaching

☐ Fishing
☐ Hiking
☐ Horseback Riding
☐ Hunting
☐ Off-Roading
☐ Paddle Boarding
☐ Photography

☐ Picknicking
☐ Rock Climbing
☐ Shooting Range
☐ Snowshoeing
☐ Stargazing
☐ Swimming
☐ Tennis

☐ Walking
☐ Wildlife Watching
☐ _____
☐ _____
☐ _____
☐ _____
☐ _____

Traveling by:

☐ ☐ ☐ ☐ ☐ ☐ ☐ ☐ ☐ ☐ ☐ ☐

RESERVATION INFORMATION:

Address: _____
_____

Reserved dates: _____

Check-in time: _____ Early check-in?: ☐ y ☐ n

Check-out time: _____ Late check-out?: ☐ y ☐ n

Website: _____

Phone: _____

WiFi: _____ WiFi password: _____

Dog friendly?: ☐ y ☐ n   Open all year?: ☐ y ☐ n

Add your favorite ticket stub, postcard, photo, stamp or drawing here

LET NEW ADVENTURES
»» BEGIN →

SEACLIFF STATE BEACH

County: Santa Cruz

Established: 1931

Acres: 89

Star Rating

☆ ☆ ☆ ☆ ☆

My favorite thing about this place is... _____

Why I went ... _____

Who I went with ... _____

When I went ... _____

What I did... _____

What I saw... _____

What I learned... _____

An unforgettable moment... _____

A laughable moment... _____

A surprising moment... _____

An unforeseeable moment... _____

Wildlife spotted... _____

List

- [ ] _____
- [ ] _____
- [ ] _____
- [ ] _____
- [ ] _____
- [ ] _____
- [ ] _____
- [ ] _____
- [ ] _____
- [ ] _____
- [ ] _____
- [ ] _____
- [ ] _____
- [ ] _____
- [ ] _____
- [ ] _____
- [ ] _____
- [ ] _____

Snapped a selfie | Location... _____

Took a park sign photo? - ☐ y ☐ n

The weather was ... ☐ ☐ ☐ ☐ ☐ ☐ ☐

PLAN YOUR TRIP:

☐ Day Trip   ☐ Overnight Stay

Reservations required: ☐ y ☐ n

Date reservations made: _____

Refund Policy: ☐ y ☐ n   Site #: _____

Confirmation #: _____

Miles to travel: _____

Time traveling: _____

RV's?: ☐ y ☐ n Largest size RV? _____

Activities Accomplished:

☐ Archery
☐ Biking
☐ Birding
☐ Boating
☐ Camping
☐ Caving
☐ Geocaching

☐ Fishing
☐ Hiking
☐ Horseback Riding
☐ Hunting
☐ Off-Roading
☐ Paddle Boarding
☐ Photography

☐ Picknicking
☐ Rock Climbing
☐ Shooting Range
☐ Snowshoeing
☐ Stargazing
☐ Swimming
☐ Tennis

☐ Walking
☐ Wildlife Watching
☐ _____
☐ _____
☐ _____
☐ _____
☐ _____

RESERVATION INFORMATION:

Address: _____
_____

Reserved dates: _____

Check-in time: _____   Early check-in?: ☐ y ☐ n

Check-out time: _____   Late check-out?: ☐ y ☐ n

Website: _____

Phone: _____

WiFi: _____   WiFi password: _____

Dog friendly?: ☐ y ☐ n   Open all year?: ☐ y ☐ n

Traveling by:

☐ ☐ ☐ ☐ ☐ ☐ ☐ ☐ ☐ ☐ ☐ ☐

Add your favorite ticket stub, postcard, photo, stamp or drawing here

LET NEW ADVENTURES
»» BEGIN →

Silver Strand State Beach

County: San Diego

Established: 1932

Acres: 3,749

Star Rating
☆ ☆ ☆ ☆ ☆

My favorite thing about this place is... _____

Why I went ... _____

Who I went with ... _____

When I went ... _____

What I did... _____

What I saw... _____

What I learned... _____

An unforgettable moment... _____

A laughable moment... _____

A surprising moment... _____

An unforeseeable moment... _____

Wildlife spotted... _____

List
- [ ] _____
- [ ] _____
- [ ] _____
- [ ] _____
- [ ] _____
- [ ] _____
- [ ] _____
- [ ] _____
- [ ] _____
- [ ] _____
- [ ] _____
- [ ] _____
- [ ] _____
- [ ] _____
- [ ] _____
- [ ] _____
- [ ] _____
- [ ] _____

Snapped a selfie | Location... _____

Took a park sign photo? - ☐ y ☐ n

The weather was ...
☐ ☐ ☐ ☐ ☐ ☐ ☐

PLAN YOUR TRIP:

☐ Day Trip   ☐ Overnight Stay

Reservations required: ☐ y ☐ n

Date reservations made: _____

Refund Policy: ☐ y ☐ n   Site #: _____

Confirmation #: _____

Miles to travel: _____

Time traveling: _____

RV's?: ☐ y ☐ n Largest size RV? _____

Activities Accomplished:

☐ Archery
☐ Biking
☐ Birding
☐ Boating
☐ Camping
☐ Caving
☐ Geocaching

☐ Fishing
☐ Hiking
☐ Horseback Riding
☐ Hunting
☐ Off-Roading
☐ Paddle Boarding
☐ Photography

☐ Picknicking
☐ Rock Climbing
☐ Shooting Range
☐ Snowshoeing
☐ Stargazing
☐ Swimming
☐ Tennis

☐ Walking
☐ Wildlife Watching
☐ _____
☐ _____
☐ _____
☐ _____
☐ _____

RESERVATION INFORMATION:

Address: _____
_____

Reserved dates: _____

Check-in time: _____   Early check-in?: ☐ y ☐ n

Check-out time: _____   Late check-out?: ☐ y ☐ n

Website: _____

Phone: _____

WiFi: _____   WiFi password: _____

Dog friendly?: ☐ y ☐ n   Open all year?: ☐ y ☐ n

Traveling by:

☐ ☐ ☐ ☐ ☐ ☐ ☐ ☐ ☐ ☐ ☐ ☐

Add your favorite ticket stub, postcard, photo, stamp or drawing here

LET NEW ADVENTURES
»» BEGIN →

SOUTH CARLSBAD STATE BEACH

County: San Diego

Established: 1949

Acres: 118

Star Rating
☆ ☆ ☆ ☆ ☆

My favorite thing about this place is... _____

Why I went ... _____

Who I went with ... _____

When I went ... _____

What I did... _____

What I saw... _____

What I learned... _____

An unforgettable moment... _____

A laughable moment... _____

A surprising moment... _____

An unforeseeable moment... _____

Wildlife spotted... _____

List
- ☐ _____
- ☐ _____
- ☐ _____
- ☐ _____
- ☐ _____
- ☐ _____
- ☐ _____
- ☐ _____
- ☐ _____
- ☐ _____
- ☐ _____
- ☐ _____
- ☐ _____
- ☐ _____
- ☐ _____
- ☐ _____
- ☐ _____
- ☐ _____
- ☐ _____

Snapped a selfie | Location...

Took a park sign photo? - ☐ y ☐ n

The weather was ...
☐ ☐ ☐ ☐ ☐ ☐ ☐

PLAN YOUR TRIP:

RESERVATION INFORMATION:

☐ Day Trip   ☐ Overnight Stay

Reservations required: ☐y ☐n

Date reservations made: _____

Refund Policy: ☐y ☐n   Site #: _____

Confirmation #: _____

Miles to travel: _____

Time traveling: _____

RV's?: ☐y ☐n Largest size RV? _____

Address: _____
_____

Reserved dates: _____

Check-in time: _____ Early check-in?: ☐y ☐n

Check-out time: _____ Late check-out?: ☐y ☐n

Website: _____

Phone: _____

WiFi: _____ WiFi password: _____

Dog friendly?: ☐y ☐n   Open all year?: ☐y ☐n

Activities Accomplished:

☐ Archery
☐ Biking
☐ Birding
☐ Boating
☐ Camping
☐ Caving
☐ Geocaching

☐ Fishing
☐ Hiking
☐ Horseback Riding
☐ Hunting
☐ Off-Roading
☐ Paddle Boarding
☐ Photography

☐ Picknicking
☐ Rock Climbing
☐ Shooting Range
☐ Snowshoeing
☐ Stargazing
☐ Swimming
☐ Tennis

☐ Walking
☐ Wildlife Watching
☐ _____
☐ _____
☐ _____
☐ _____
☐ _____

Traveling by:

☐ ☐ ☐ ☐ ☐ ☐ ☐ ☐ ☐ ☐ ☐ ☐

Add your favorite ticket stub, postcard, photo, stamp or drawing here

LET NEW ADVENTURES
»» BEGIN →

SUNSET STATE BEACH

County: Santa Cruz

Established: 1931   *Acres: 302*

Star Rating

☆ ☆ ☆ ☆ ☆

My favorite thing about this place is... _____

Why I went ... _____

Who I went with ... _____

When I went ... _____

What I did... _____

What I saw... _____

What I learned... _____

List
☐ _____
☐ _____
☐ _____
☐ _____
☐ _____
☐ _____
☐ _____
☐ _____
☐ _____
☐ _____
☐ _____
☐ _____
☐ _____
☐ _____
☐ _____
☐ _____
☐ _____
☐ _____

An unforgettable moment... _____

A laughable moment... _____

A surprising moment... _____

An unforeseeable moment... _____

Wildlife spotted... _____

Snapped a selfie | Location... _____

Took a park sign photo? - ☐ y ☐ n

The weather was ...
☐ ☐ ☐ ☐ ☐ ☐ ☐

PLAN YOUR TRIP:

☐ Day Trip   ☐ Overnight Stay

Reservations required: ☐ y ☐ n

Date reservations made: _____

Refund Policy: ☐ y ☐ n   Site #: _____

Confirmation #: _____

Miles to travel: _____

Time traveling: _____

RV's?: ☐ y ☐ n Largest size RV? _____

Activities Accomplished:

☐ Archery
☐ Biking
☐ Birding
☐ Boating
☐ Camping
☐ Caving
☐ Geocaching

☐ Fishing
☐ Hiking
☐ Horseback Riding
☐ Hunting
☐ Off-Roading
☐ Paddle Boarding
☐ Photography

☐ Picknicking
☐ Rock Climbing
☐ Shooting Range
☐ Snowshoeing
☐ Stargazing
☐ Swimming
☐ Tennis

☐ Walking
☐ Wildlife Watching
☐ _____
☐ _____
☐ _____
☐ _____
☐ _____

RESERVATION INFORMATION:

Address: _____
_____

Reserved dates: _____

Check-in time: _____   Early check-in?: ☐ y ☐ n

Check-out time: _____   Late check-out?: ☐ y ☐ n

Website: _____

Phone: _____

WiFi: _____   WiFi password: _____

Dog friendly?: ☐ y ☐ n   Open all year?: ☐ y ☐ n

Traveling by:

☐ ☐ ☐ ☐ ☐ ☐ ☐ ☐ ☐ ☐ ☐ ☐

Add your favorite ticket stub, postcard, photo, stamp or drawing here

LET NEW ADVENTURES
≫ BEGIN →

THORNTON STATE BEACH

County: San Mateo

Established: 1955

Acres: 58

Star Rating
☆☆☆☆☆

My favorite thing about this place is...

Why I went ...

Who I went with ...

When I went ...

What I did...

What I saw...

What I learned...

An unforgettable moment...

A laughable moment...

A surprising moment...

An unforeseeable moment...

Wildlife spotted...

List

- [ ]
- [ ]
- [ ]
- [ ]
- [ ]
- [ ]
- [ ]
- [ ]
- [ ]
- [ ]
- [ ]
- [ ]
- [ ]
- [ ]
- [ ]
- [ ]
- [ ]
- [ ]

Snapped a selfie | Location...

Took a park sign photo? - ☐ y ☐ n

The weather was ...
☐ ☐ ☐ ☐ ☐ ☐ ☐

PLAN YOUR TRIP:

RESERVATION INFORMATION:

☐ Day Trip　　　　☐ Overnight Stay

Reservations required: ☐ y ☐ n

Date reservations made: _____

Refund Policy: ☐ y ☐ n　Site #: _____

Confirmation #: _____

Miles to travel: _____

Time traveling: _____

RV's?: ☐ y ☐ n Largest size RV? _____

Address: _____
_____

Reserved dates: _____

Check-in time: _____　Early check-in?: ☐ y ☐ n

Check-out time: _____　Late check-out?: ☐ y ☐ n

Website: _____

Phone: _____

WiFi: _____　WiFi password: _____

Dog friendly?: ☐ y ☐ n　　Open all year?: ☐ y ☐ n

Activities Accomplished:

☐ Archery
☐ Biking
☐ Birding
☐ Boating
☐ Camping
☐ Caving
☐ Geocaching

☐ Fishing
☐ Hiking
☐ Horseback Riding
☐ Hunting
☐ Off-Roading
☐ Paddle Boarding
☐ Photography

☐ Picknicking
☐ Rock Climbing
☐ Shooting Range
☐ Snowshoeing
☐ Stargazing
☐ Swimming
☐ Tennis

☐ Walking
☐ Wildlife Watching
☐ _____
☐ _____
☐ _____
☐ _____
☐ _____

Traveling by:

☐　☐　☐　☐　☐　☐　☐　☐　☐　☐　☐　☐

Add your favorite ticket stub, postcard, photo, stamp or drawing here

LET NEW ADVENTURES
» BEGIN →

TORREY PINES STATE BEACH

County: San Diego

Established: 1952

Acres: 61

Star Rating
☆ ☆ ☆ ☆ ☆

My favorite thing about this place is... _____

Why I went ... _____

Who I went with ... _____

When I went ... _____

What I did... _____

What I saw... _____

What I learned... _____

An unforgettable moment... _____

A laughable moment... _____

A surprising moment... _____

An unforeseeable moment... _____

Wildlife spotted... _____

Snapped a selfie | Location... _____

Took a park sign photo? - ☐ y ☐ n

List

☐ _____
☐ _____
☐ _____
☐ _____
☐ _____
☐ _____
☐ _____
☐ _____
☐ _____
☐ _____
☐ _____
☐ _____
☐ _____
☐ _____
☐ _____
☐ _____
☐ _____
☐ _____
☐ _____
☐ _____

The weather was ...
☐ ☐ ☐ ☐ ☐ ☐ ☐

PLAN YOUR TRIP:

☐ Day Trip   ☐ Overnight Stay

Reservations required: ☐ y ☐ n

Date reservations made: _____

Refund Policy: ☐ y ☐ n   Site #: _____

Confirmation #: _____

Miles to travel: _____

Time traveling: _____

RV's?: ☐ y ☐ n Largest size RV? _____

Activities Accomplished:

☐ Archery	☐ Fishing	☐ Picknicking	☐ Walking
☐ Biking	☐ Hiking	☐ Rock Climbing	☐ Wildlife Watching
☐ Birding	☐ Horseback Riding	☐ Shooting Range	☐ _____
☐ Boating	☐ Hunting	☐ Snowshoeing	☐ _____
☐ Camping	☐ Off-Roading	☐ Stargazing	☐ _____
☐ Caving	☐ Paddle Boarding	☐ Swimming	☐ _____
☐ Geocaching	☐ Photography	☐ Tennis	☐ _____

RESERVATION INFORMATION:

Address: _____
_____

Reserved dates: _____

Check-in time: _____   Early check-in?: ☐ y ☐ n

Check-out time: _____   Late check-out?: ☐ y ☐ n

Website: _____

Phone: _____

WiFi: _____   WiFi password: _____

Dog friendly?: ☐ y ☐ n   Open all year?: ☐ y ☐ n

Traveling by:

☐   ☐   ☐   ☐   ☐   ☐   ☐   ☐   ☐   ☐   ☐   ☐

Add your favorite ticket stub, postcard, photo, stamp or drawing here

LET NEW ADVENTURES ≫ BEGIN →

Trinidad State Beach

County: Humboldt

Established: 1937   *Acres: 159*

Star Rating
☆☆☆☆☆

My favorite thing about this place is... _____

Why I went ... _____

Who I went with ... _____

When I went ... _____

What I did... _____

What I saw... _____

What I learned... _____

An unforgettable moment... _____

A laughable moment... _____

A surprising moment... _____

An unforeseeable moment... _____

Wildlife spotted... _____

List

- ☐ _____
- ☐ _____
- ☐ _____
- ☐ _____
- ☐ _____
- ☐ _____
- ☐ _____
- ☐ _____
- ☐ _____
- ☐ _____
- ☐ _____
- ☐ _____
- ☐ _____
- ☐ _____
- ☐ _____
- ☐ _____
- ☐ _____
- ☐ _____
- ☐ _____

Snapped a selfie | Location... _____

Took a park sign photo? - ☐ y ☐ n

The weather was ... ☐ ☐ ☐ ☐ ☐ ☐ ☐

PLAN YOUR TRIP:

RESERVATION INFORMATION:

☐ Day Trip   ☐ Overnight Stay

Reservations required: ☐ y ☐ n

Date reservations made: _____

Refund Policy: ☐ y ☐ n Site #: _____

Confirmation #: _____

Miles to travel: _____

Time traveling: _____

RV's?: ☐ y ☐ n Largest size RV? _____

Address: _____
_____

Reserved dates: _____

Check-in time: _____ Early check-in?: ☐ y ☐ n

Check-out time: _____ Late check-out?: ☐ y ☐ n

Website: _____

Phone: _____

WiFi: _____ WiFi password: _____

Dog friendly?: ☐ y ☐ n   Open all year?: ☐ y ☐ n

Activities Accomplished:

☐ Archery
☐ Biking
☐ Birding
☐ Boating
☐ Camping
☐ Caving
☐ Geocaching

☐ Fishing
☐ Hiking
☐ Horseback Riding
☐ Hunting
☐ Off-Roading
☐ Paddle Boarding
☐ Photography

☐ Picknicking
☐ Rock Climbing
☐ Shooting Range
☐ Snowshoeing
☐ Stargazing
☐ Swimming
☐ Tennis

☐ Walking
☐ Wildlife Watching
☐ _____
☐ _____
☐ _____
☐ _____
☐ _____

Traveling by:

☐ ☐ ☐ ☐ ☐ ☐ ☐ ☐ ☐ ☐ ☐ ☐

Add your favorite ticket stub, postcard, photo, stamp or drawing here

LET NEW ADVENTURES
≫ BEGIN →

Twin Lakes State Beach

County: Santa Cruz

Established: 1955

Acres: 95

Star Rating
☆ ☆ ☆ ☆ ☆

My favorite thing about this place is... _____

Why I went ... _____

Who I went with ... _____

When I went ... _____

What I did... _____

What I saw... _____

What I learned... _____

An unforgettable moment... _____

A laughable moment... _____

A surprising moment... _____

An unforeseeable moment... _____

Wildlife spotted... _____

List
- ☐ _____
- ☐ _____
- ☐ _____
- ☐ _____
- ☐ _____
- ☐ _____
- ☐ _____
- ☐ _____
- ☐ _____
- ☐ _____
- ☐ _____
- ☐ _____
- ☐ _____
- ☐ _____
- ☐ _____
- ☐ _____
- ☐ _____
- ☐ _____

Snapped a selfie | Location... _____

Took a park sign photo? - ☐ y ☐ n

The weather was ...
☐ ☐ ☐ ☐ ☐ ☐ ☐

PLAN YOUR TRIP:

RESERVATION INFORMATION:

☐ Day Trip   ☐ Overnight Stay

Reservations required: ☐ y ☐ n

Date reservations made: _____

Refund Policy: ☐ y ☐ n Site #: _____

Confirmation #: _____

Miles to travel: _____

Time traveling: _____

RV's?: ☐ y ☐ n Largest size RV? _____

Address: _____
_____

Reserved dates: _____

Check-in time: _____ Early check-in?: ☐ y ☐ n

Check-out time: _____ Late check-out?: ☐ y ☐ n

Website: _____

Phone: _____

WiFi: _____ WiFi password: _____

Dog friendly?: ☐ y ☐ n   Open all year?: ☐ y ☐ n

Activities Accomplished:

☐ Archery
☐ Biking
☐ Birding
☐ Boating
☐ Camping
☐ Caving
☐ Geocaching

☐ Fishing
☐ Hiking
☐ Horseback Riding
☐ Hunting
☐ Off-Roading
☐ Paddle Boarding
☐ Photography

☐ Picknicking
☐ Rock Climbing
☐ Shooting Range
☐ Snowshoeing
☐ Stargazing
☐ Swimming
☐ Tennis

☐ Walking
☐ Wildlife Watching
☐ _____
☐ _____
☐ _____
☐ _____
☐ _____

Traveling by:

☐   ☐   ☐   ☐   ☐   ☐   ☐   ☐   ☐   ☐   ☐   ☐

Add your favorite ticket stub, postcard, photo, stamp or drawing here

LET NEW ADVENTURES
» BEGIN →

WESTPORT-UNION LANDING STATE BEACH

County: Mendocino

Established: 1952　　　　　　　　　　　　　　　　*Acres:* 58

Star Rating
☆☆☆☆☆

My favorite thing about this place is... _____

Why I went ... _____

Who I went with ... _____

When I went ... _____

What I did... _____

What I saw... _____

What I learned... _____

An unforgettable moment... _____

A laughable moment... _____

A surprising moment... _____

An unforeseeable moment... _____

Wildlife spotted... _____

📷 Snapped a selfie | Location... _____

📷 Took a park sign photo? - ☐ y ☐ n

List
☐ _____
☐ _____
☐ _____
☐ _____
☐ _____
☐ _____
☐ _____
☐ _____
☐ _____
☐ _____
☐ _____
☐ _____
☐ _____
☐ _____
☐ _____
☐ _____
☐ _____
☐ _____

The weather was ...
☐ ☐ ☐ ☐ ☐ ☐ ☐

PLAN YOUR TRIP:

RESERVATION INFORMATION:

☐ Day Trip   ☐ Overnight Stay

Reservations required: ☐ y ☐ n

Date reservations made: _____

Refund Policy: ☐ y ☐ n Site #: _____

Confirmation #: _____

Miles to travel: _____

Time traveling: _____

RV's?: ☐ y ☐ n Largest size RV? _____

Activities Accomplished:

Address: _____
_____

Reserved dates: _____

Check-in time: _____ Early check-in?: ☐ y ☐ n

Check-out time: _____ Late check-out?: ☐ y ☐ n

Website: _____

Phone: _____

WiFi: _____ WiFi password: _____

Dog friendly?: ☐ y ☐ n   Open all year?: ☐ y ☐ n

☐ Archery
☐ Biking
☐ Birding
☐ Boating
☐ Camping
☐ Caving
☐ Geocaching

☐ Fishing
☐ Hiking
☐ Horseback Riding
☐ Hunting
☐ Off-Roading
☐ Paddle Boarding
☐ Photography

☐ Picknicking
☐ Rock Climbing
☐ Shooting Range
☐ Snowshoeing
☐ Stargazing
☐ Swimming
☐ Tennis

☐ Walking
☐ Wildlife Watching
☐ _____
☐ _____
☐ _____
☐ _____
☐ _____

Traveling by:

☐ ☐ ☐ ☐ ☐ ☐ ☐ ☐ ☐ ☐ ☐ ☐

Add your favorite ticket stub, postcard, photo, stamp or drawing here

LET NEW ADVENTURES
≫ BEGIN →

WILL ROGERS STATE BEACH

County: Los Angeles

Established: 1931

Acres: 82

Star Rating
☆ ☆ ☆ ☆ ☆

My favorite thing about this place is... _____

Why I went ... _____

Who I went with ... _____

When I went ... _____

What I did... _____

What I saw... _____

What I learned... _____

An unforgettable moment... _____

A laughable moment... _____

A surprising moment... _____

An unforeseeable moment... _____

Wildlife spotted... _____

📷 Snapped a selfie | Location... _____

📷 Took a park sign photo? - ☐ y ☐ n

List

☐ _____
☐ _____
☐ _____
☐ _____
☐ _____
☐ _____
☐ _____
☐ _____
☐ _____
☐ _____
☐ _____
☐ _____
☐ _____
☐ _____
☐ _____
☐ _____
☐ _____
☐ _____

The weather was ...
☐ ☐ ☐ ☐ ☐ ☐ ☐

PLAN YOUR TRIP:

☐ Day Trip   ☐ Overnight Stay

Reservations required: ☐ y ☐ n

Date reservations made: _____

Refund Policy: ☐ y ☐ n   Site #: _____

Confirmation #: _____

Miles to travel: _____

Time traveling: _____

RV's?: ☐ y ☐ n Largest size RV? _____

Activities Accomplished:

☐ Archery
☐ Biking
☐ Birding
☐ Boating
☐ Camping
☐ Caving
☐ Geocaching

☐ Fishing
☐ Hiking
☐ Horseback Riding
☐ Hunting
☐ Off-Roading
☐ Paddle Boarding
☐ Photography

☐ Picknicking
☐ Rock Climbing
☐ Shooting Range
☐ Snowshoeing
☐ Stargazing
☐ Swimming
☐ Tennis

☐ Walking
☐ Wildlife Watching
☐ _____
☐ _____
☐ _____
☐ _____
☐ _____

Traveling by:

☐ ☐ ☐ ☐ ☐ ☐ ☐ ☐ ☐ ☐ ☐ ☐

RESERVATION INFORMATION:

Address: _____
_____

Reserved dates: _____

Check-in time: _____   Early check-in?: ☐ y ☐ n

Check-out time: _____   Late check-out?: ☐ y ☐ n

Website: _____

Phone: _____

WiFi: _____   WiFi password: _____

Dog friendly?: ☐ y ☐ n   Open all year?: ☐ y ☐ n

Add your favorite ticket stub, postcard, photo, stamp or drawing here

LET NEW ADVENTURES
≫ BEGIN →

ZMUDOWSKI STATE BEACH

County: Monterey and Santa Cruz

Established: 1950

Acres: 194

Star Rating
☆ ☆ ☆ ☆ ☆

My favorite thing about this place is... _____

Why I went ... _____

Who I went with ... _____

When I went ... _____

What I did... _____

What I saw... _____

What I learned... _____

An unforgettable moment... _____

A laughable moment... _____

A surprising moment... _____

An unforeseeable moment... _____

Wildlife spotted... _____

Snapped a selfie | Location... _____

Took a park sign photo? - ☐ y ☐ n

List

☐ _____
☐ _____
☐ _____
☐ _____
☐ _____
☐ _____
☐ _____
☐ _____
☐ _____
☐ _____
☐ _____
☐ _____
☐ _____
☐ _____
☐ _____
☐ _____
☐ _____
☐ _____

The weather was ...
☐ ☐ ☐ ☐ ☐ ☐ ☐